THE SYSTEM AND REVOLUTION

V. A. SHIVA

Dr. V. A. Shiva Ayyadurai

To Heaven on Earth

Printed in the United States of America.

First Edition, 2016.

ISBN 978-0-9970402-2-7

General Interactive, LLC
Publishing Division
701 Concord Ave.
Cambridge, MA 02138
www.generalinteractive.com

All proceeds from the sale of this book go to Innovation Corps, a 501 (c) not-for-profit project.
www.innovation-corps.org

CONTENTS

Why Read This Book?

We have Bread, but no Health; we have Land, but no Freedom; we have "Peace," but no Truth. For Truth, Freedom and Health, we need Revolution. And, to make Revolution, you need a practical understanding of the principles of *all* Systems. This book will teach you those principles, in a practical way, by using your body as a system. Health and wellbeing will be a result, but more importantly, what you will really learn are the unifying principles of all Systems, which will provide you the knowledge to make Revolution on *any* System, here and now.

V. A. SHIVA
Paris, France
April, 2016

INTRODUCTION

What Is To Be Done?

"You have nothing to lose but your chains ...."

I'm starting this book with a quote from Karl Marx. Is that outrageous? Is it inflammatory? I hope so!

I have four degrees from MIT but I don't want to be the smart boy scientist in khakis and a sport shirt giving a TED talk and then going out for a cappuccino.

One of the themes of this book will be the relationship between the center and the periphery – in a human cell, in a human body, and in all aspects of human affairs, and the realization that there actually is no "center" but one that has been imposed on us from "above."

I was definitely born in the periphery, the child of a lower caste family in India where my grandmother was a spiritual healer. But, I don't want to be a wise and gentle guru telling you about the Hindu god with the head of an elephant.

Here's what I do want. But it's more than "want." It's "need." I need to tell you about what I've learned in my unique education and in my even more unique life experiences.

Why do I need that? It's not to stoke my ego. It's not to be on television. It's because a time for change – radical change – has arrived and I have a role to play at this historic moment. I have tools to provide. Not physical tools, but vital information for this opportunity so that we don't blow it.

I feel like I've been given an assignment. I've been cast in a role, and it's not an easy one to fulfill. I have to tell people the truth – and when they don't believe me I have to change their minds.

I invented the first authentic, comprehensive email system when I was a 14-year-old working as a Research Fellow at the University of Medicine and Dentistry of New Jersey. That's the truth but it's a controversial statement. I've been called "delusional."

So why don't I just forget about it? Why don't I shut up about it?

Here's why. That experience took place in the cultural context of growing up as a lower-caste Indian kid where my earliest memories as a four year old was being segregated and given water in a different bowl from my "upper caste friends" and emigrating from the extremes of Bombay and a small south Indian rural village Muhavur in Tamil Nadu to Newark, New Jersey. It was part of a timeline that included observing my grandmother's practice of Siddha, an ancient system of medicine and healing and also attending an elite program in computer science at NYU's Courant Institute of Mathematical Sciences while still in high school.

It's very true that I haven't followed the standard nerd script and said, "Aw shucks" – but it's not because I'm delusional. On the contrary, I've been stripped of all delusions about how things work for innovators who don't fit the mold.

What's really delusional are people inside a centralized academic, corporate, or government environment sitting in judgment of me when I'm a creature of the periphery. That's an entirely different setting and I'm a different kind of person in every way.

It's also delusional for those in controlling positions in academia, business, or government to imagine I'm not going to share my experiences in order to ignite radical and positive change.

Yes, I am a revolutionary. I was five years old when a friend of my father's came to our home and said poor villagers were taking up arms against their landowners. He said the villagers didn't have any money and didn't have any food and didn't have any clothes.

So I said, "But that's wrong."

The man told my father, "Your son is a communist."

"Don't worry," my father said. "When he gets older he'll change."

But I haven't changed. My anger – no, my hatred – has only exponentially increased against those who rule through exploitation, influence, and intimidation. Priests, saints, gurus, and therapists all advise us against hating our enemies, but millions of people can't afford that luxury. Meanwhile, those wise counselors are profiting, directly or indirectly, as servants of the enemy who we're not supposed to hate.

I have learned about the enemy. I've known all about the manipulative dogmas and doctrines we're fed every day. I reached the highest levels of academia. I've appeared in front of audiences with bestselling New Age authors. I lived in Hollywood and rubbed shoulder with narcissistic celebrities whose concern for climate change or some social cause was all about getting lots of Tweets and re-Tweets.

I've held a high position in the Indian government. I saw how a feudal, colonialist mentality still pervades that country at a cost of billions. I've seen how so-called eminent scientists and major American medical research institutions really work. Their first concern is getting funding for their pet projects, securing tenure or getting some paper published. Curing a disease is largely an afterthought.

So I've learned from the enemy and I've also fought them my whole life. There's a dramatic photo of my burning the South African flag as a 17-year-old undergraduate on the steps of the MIT Student Center. I had just led a major protest against MIT's investments in apartheid South Africa. I challenged the MIT administration to provide proper wages for food service workers and to increase enrollment for poor students, women and minorities. At my PhD graduation, I was the only one who raised a banner "US Out of Iraq" demanding an end to the US invasion. Half the crowd cheered and the other half booed me. I exposed corruption at the highest scientific institution in India, and was forced to flee India. I've fought the Raytheon Corporation about my rightful place in history for the invention of email. I'm now fighting Monsanto to expose the lack of safety standards in GMOs.

So, it's not just an intellectual pursuit. I want to fight these forces of evil, because that is what they are. I want you to join me in that fight. I want to share, in this book, my weapons – the weapons I've learned from the enemy.

What's my most powerful weapon? What's the weapon that can finally win? It's not a gun or a bomb. It's the science of systems. It's seeing and really understanding how things are connected. And it's also seeing all the traps and distractions that are put in your way.

Here's the best part. Once you learn this science – once enough people understand it – we can create an army that will win the war. Which is the first thing they don't want you to know!

To distract you, to keep you feeling small and helpless, what they want to do is indoctrinate you. They want to "convert" you because, as Marx said, "Religion is the opiate of the people."

Religion? Yes, that's right – because, take my word for it, you've been indoctrinated, and very possibly converted, by one of the "religions" that control how we relate to our thoughts, our feelings, our bodies, our health, our work, our relationships, our education, our future, our past, our present, and virtually everything in our lives.

You've been scammed by the priesthoods whose dogmas falsify who you are and what you are. Those priesthoods are powerful and convincing. They're smart, well-funded, and ruthless. They want your money, but that's only the first step.

What they really want is power over you. They want you to bow down. And it's working. Millions of people are bowing down and there's an excellent chance you've been one of them. But you're ready to change. I know you are, because if you weren't, you wouldn't be reading a book with _revolution_ in its title.

The largest and most powerful of these soul-crushing doctrines is a reductionist science that fragments reality and somehow manages to make things seem both simpler and more complicated than they really are. I say this as a scientist whose education from the Massachusetts Institute of Technology spans multiple disciplines: electrical engineering, mechanical engineering, architecture, and biological engineering.

We'll look very closely at reductionism and its effects in subsequent chapters.

Seemingly opposite to reductionist science – but actually complementary to it – is the sentimental mysticism of gurus, miracles, and manifestations from the universe. (And once again, I say this as someone who grew up right in the midst of the ancient wisdom and traditions of India.)

In popular culture, this doctrine is called the "New Age" category. It draws on non-denominational religion – "spirituality"– rather than science. There may be some watered down references to Galileo or Einstein, but basically things just happen for a very self-centered and sentimental reason. We may not know exactly why or how, but that doesn't really matter. The hugely successful book (and video) called _The Secret_ was based on the idea that we can attract success, money, or whatever into our lives by thinking about it or wanting it.

14

Exactly how that works is beyond our understanding, but so what? It sounds beautiful, and that's all you need to know. Might as well take an aspirin or Valium, to lull us into peace, harmony and oblivion.

Both reductionist science and New Age proselytizers have their own priesthoods, rituals, commandments, and taboos. Those rules and regulations are actually the most important things about those dogmas, because neither of them can really describe (much less solve) many of the most important problems of our lives.

The word "spirituality" has also been abused and manipulated by this priesthood. The true and greatest spiritual leaders consistently addressed the issues of the here and now, and challenged the centralization of power and authority. For them, Heaven was not distinct from Earth. In the Hindu tradition, the great Shankaracharya asked a fundamental question, "If there is equality in heaven, why isn't there equality on earth?" That question in the 8th century gave rise to the Bhakthi Movement, one based on devotion and love that led to early breakdowns of the caste system (which were later reversed by the brutality of colonialism starting in the 17th century).

Jesus also addressed the here and now. He whipped the moneylenders in the temple. Yes, whipped them. He got angry, and threw them out. He perturbed the religious hierarchy, which was subjugating the masses. These political issues, however, are never discussed in churches and written off as some anomaly of Jesus' behavior. But the essence of Jesus' teachings was justice, truth and love for all, here and now, "… it is easier for a camel to go through the eye of a needle than for a rich person to enter the Kingdom of God!" A real spiritualist is a revolutionary. To sit by and speak of spiritual enlightenment and watch one's brothers and sisters and you be subjugated to lies, exploitation, and pale reductionist aspects of truth is inhuman and non-spiritual.

A hundred years ago, Vladimir Lenin led the Russian revolution with the slogan "Peace, Land, and Bread." Peace meant ending Russia's involvement in World War I. Land meant redistributing aristocrats' estates to the peasants. Bread meant an end to food shortages and starvation. Today we have our own version of "land" – which means an abundance of material possessions for a small number of people, and a fanatical desire to possess them by a multitude of others. We have "bread" – which means enough to eat, even if it's often unhealthy and is simply another resource for corporate profit.

Most disturbingly, we also have the current version of "peace" – which is simply an anesthetized numbness or a bewildering blindness, perpetuated by that priesthood. Whether it's in politics, organized religion, healthcare, or a hundred other areas of our lives, we're in the dark and we don't even know it. This goes much further than that famous line from *The Wizard of Oz*, "Pay no attention to the man behind the curtain." We've been taught that there isn't any curtain, much less a man.

But pointing out all the problems is only the first step. The next step is action. What is to be done?

In order to introduce the principles of systems theory in the most grounded and practical way, this book will show how the human body – *your body* – is a system. Once you understand the dynamics of a system in your physical self, you'll see how it occurs everywhere. When you gain a revolutionary perspective about who and what you are as an interconnected system of systems that follow fundamental principles, you'll be able to apply that revolutionary perspective to your life and the world as a whole.

Revolution is an essential part of systems theory, and revolution isn't incremental. It's about clearly seeing the current situation, setting goals for positive change, and taking action in that direction. It's not a matter of saying everything is perfect now or everything will be perfect – because that's just another way of talking ourselves out of taking action. Perfection is not the goal, but rather a commitment to the goal, no matter how seemingly impossible the goal may seem, and to take deliberate and conscious action to achieve that goal.

Previous revolutionaries did not do everything perfectly, but that doesn't mean we shouldn't take revolutionary action ourselves. Plus, we have information and technologies that they didn't have. Creating email would have been impossible before there was computer code, and many people said it was still impossible. But something is "impossible" only until it happens. It was impossible for Mike Tyson to get knocked out. But once he got knocked out, "Oh yeah, I guess it actually was possible."

The foundation principle of an engineering system is to keep getting better – not to be perfect immediately, but to improve. That's also the underlying principle of this book. If it seems impossible to do it perfectly at this point in time, or if it failed in the past, that doesn't mean we don't do it.

The compelling forces that drive human history forward are the desire for truth, freedom and health. We've failed, and we're also getting better at it. The Wright brothers' first aircraft only flew for twelve seconds, but we don't criticize the Wright brothers because they didn't create a space shuttle.

The following are five key principles of a systems perspective on revolutionary change:

1. We must know how things are interconnected in the world. The interconnections matter more than the parts. We must understand the connection between the center and the periphery, and we must look beyond the centralized command-and-control model to realize there is no "center."

2. Truth emerges when the whole is greater than the sum of the parts.

3. Real change is rapid and fast when a "critical mass" or boiling point has been achieved. At exactly 212 degrees Fahrenheit, water starts vaporizing because particles are moving in the same direction. It's sudden, fast and irreversible. The movement or "transport" of mass literally creates, what we say in science, "a phase transition" – a Revolution.

4. We need an accurate and reality-based feedback process that allows for the tracking of clearly set goals and indicates when they have been achieved, and when we are off course. This feedback process allows us to repeat, adjust, or end our input behavior.

5. There is no belief or aspiration to perfection. There is commitment to a goal and a commitment to iterate toward the goal, and the goal emerges from the

interaction of the system with itself and its neighboring systems.

We will be revisiting these principles throughout the book. But a major point should be made right here. If our worthwhile goals are set, but those goals are unacceptable to the currently prevailing system, our goals cannot be achieved until the goals of the currently prevailing system are disabled or seized. And the goals of the currently prevailing system are quite straightforward: maximize profit, expand markets, monopolize and control resources, and continue along these lines indefinitely.

So what are our goals? Let's recall the slogan of the Russian revolution: Peace, Land, and Bread. Today, we have Bread but not Health. We have Land but no Freedom. Our Peace is without Truth.

To begin moving toward goals of genuine Truth, Freedom and Health, this book will introduce a systems approach to your own body and how it works. This will open up to a wider recognition that Health requires Freedom, and Freedom demands Truth to control our destiny.

Are you committed to Truth, Freedom and Health? Is that why you've chosen to read this book?

Then join me in creating this revolution. We have nothing to lose but our chains.

PART ONE

The System

CHAPTER ONE

Systems Theory: An Overview

Einstein said, "God doesn't play dice with the universe."

He was referring to the seemingly random nature of quantum mechanics, but his message can also apply to the everyday world. It seems like a reassuring message, because the ups and downs of our lives can seem chaotic.

But if the universe isn't a dice game, what is it? Systems theory offers an answer. The basics are easy to understand, and as you learn more, you'll start to see what "not playing dice" really means.

A system is a set of objects or energies working together for a specific goal or purpose. Your car is a system with thousands of components. Your cell phone is another.

Systems can be simple or complex. Washing machines, clocks, pencil sharpeners, even the solar system and the whole universe are systems. Your body is a system with many subsystems inside it.

There are only two basic classes of systems. Once you understand how they work, you can understand how *everything* works. And as Einstein said, it's not a dice game. It's not just one random thing after another. Everything is connected, and you'll see what that means once you know what to look for.

Every system in the universe is either an *open loop system* or a *closed loop system*. Both kinds of systems have five basic elements:

- Input
- Transport
- Conversion
- Structure
- Output

The image below illustrates the five elements of an open loop system. *Input* refers to what goes into the system, which can be information, energy, or physical matter. *Transport* indicates the movement or flow of *Input* through the system. *Conversion* is the transformation of *Input* into final *Output*, which again may be matter, energy or information. *Structure* refers to the form and boundaries of a system that gives it definition and sustainability, as the bones and muscles do for a human body.

Open Loop System

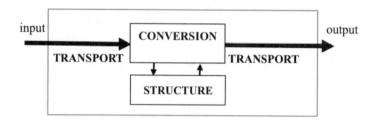

It's called an open loop system because it's permanently open to Input. An electric heater is a good example of an open loop system. Activating the heater sends an Input of electric current into the heater. Transport is the aspect of the system that moves electric and thermal energy within the system. Conversion, represented by the heating coils, transforms the electrical energy into heat. The Structure element forms and contains the entire system. Heat is the final Output.

Once the machine is turned on, the system will remain open. It will continue taking in electricity and sending out heat without any self-regulation. It will keep working at the same rate until it is turned off.

A closed loop system works differently. It includes four additional elements: a Goal; a Sensor; a Controller; and Disturbance. These elements enable a self-regulated and continuous adjustment of the Input – in order to achieve a desired Output that matches the *Goal* – in spite of *Disturbances* to the system – through the use of a *Sensor* and a *Controller*.

A closed loop system is illustrated below.

Closed Loop System

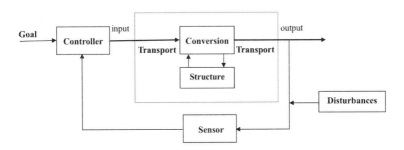

Closed loop systems are called "intelligent" because a process of self-adjustment and refinement is continually going on using the Controller, which adjusts the Input based on observing the difference between the desired Goal and the actual Output. An apartment with central heating and a thermostat is a good example. Let's say the desired temperature for the apartment is 78 degrees. That's the Goal, and the Goal is achieved when the Output of heat into the apartment is equal to the Goal.

The thermostat is the Controller. It receives information about temperature from a Sensor, the thermometer. The Controller determines the difference between the Goal and the Output. It then calculates how much Input is needed to Transport oil into the furnace for the Conversion of oil to heat. The oil tank is the Structure in which the oil is stored. If there are Disturbances (like a cold draft in the apartment) the Sensor will communicate that Disturbance to the Controller, which adjusts the Input as needed. The process continues as a closed, self-regulating, system to achieve and maintain the Goal of 78 degrees.

Here are the nine elements of a closed loop system:

- Input
- Output
- Transport
- Conversion
- Structure
- Goal
- Controller
- Sensor
- Disturbance

If you wanted to study systems at MIT, your advisor would recommend a class called *Control Systems and Feedback.* There, toward the end of the semester, you would be given the classic example of an airplane in flight as a model of highly complex systems.

An airplane in flight has important Goals. One Goal is to maintain a certain speed, say 600 miles per hour. The pilot is the Controller. The air speed indicator acting as a Sensor provides information about the plane's speed. The pilot continually notes the difference between the desired Goal of 600 miles per hour and the Output – the current speed of the plane.

If the current speed is only 500 miles per hour, the pilot, serving as the Controller, will convey a new Input that Transports fuel into the jet engines which Convert the jet fuel, which is stored in the Structure of the plane, into thrust, that increases the speed of the plane to achieve a new Output.

It may happen, however, that the engines increase the speed to only 590 miles per hour. Then the Controller – the pilot – must send a new Input signaling the need for more fuel until the speed stabilizes at 600 miles per hour. Sometimes, too, the Controller may overshoot the speed to 650 miles per hour, by having signaled a higher Input that sends too much fuel, so that Input will need to be reduced.

This feedback process is continuous and self-regulating. The Controller always assesses the Output relative to the Goal, and makes the appropriate adjustments, until the Output matches the Goal.

Sometimes, Disturbances from the environment (or another system) will occur. These Disturbances need to be observed and also fed back to the Controller. Consider the simple case of a Disturbance, such as a headwind of 100 miles per hour. Clearly, in this case the weather is another system that provides a wind Disturbance. That Disturbance will need to be accounted for in determining the Input to the engines. The pilot will have to increase the Input accordingly and proportionately to achieve the Goal of 600 miles per hour. In control systems theory, this is called "proportional control." There are many types of such Controllers.

Closed loop systems are dynamic by nature. They're always in flux. They're constantly making adjustments. "Perfection" is not a permanent condition, nor is it the "goal." It's an imaginary concept where the Goal is always being approached but is never sustained. It has to be reached for, over and over again.

One important aspect of this entire process is that though the systems may be of the same kind e.g. airplanes, the nature or system type of an airplane may be different. Different system types can be distinguished by the relative differences in the levels of Transport, Conversion and Structure elements. Being aware of these differences is essential to intelligently achieving the Goals of a system.

To illustrate this, let's continue the airplane analogy by observing three different types of airplanes: a fighter jet, a passenger plane and a military cargo plane – in short, three different types of systems.

A modern fighter jet is capable of enormous speeds, has to be fast, nimble, quick and needs to be able to make rapid changes in direction, but it also needs constant maintenance. The pilot in this case serves to be the Controller, as his or her ability to respond to Sensor feedback and Disturbances are critical to winning a battle. The fighter jet is a system whose Transport elements, the aspect of movement, are relatively more dominant than its Conversion and Structure elements. As the jet interacts with external elements like bumps on the landing strip or turbulence in the air, its powerful but delicate Transport mechanisms require attention. Such components can easily go out of balance. It's not that there's anything fundamentally wrong. It's just the nature of a high-speed plane that the Transport elements can't be perfected and permanently stabilized.

A modern passenger plane is a very different type of system than a fighter jet. The passenger plane needs to be able to move hundreds of customers in a very safe and cost effective manner. Fuel efficiency in this respect is important if an airline is going to stay in business. This demands that in such planes, great care is put into the Conversion element, such as the jet engines, to process fuel and generate thrust as efficiently as possible. Although the human pilots do actively supervise takeoffs and landings, the plane automatically flies itself to a large degree to optimize the use of fuel. In systems terminology, the pilots no longer perform the Controller or Sensor functions. The Goal is set, and the plane does the rest. While this has many advantages, if the plane's computers become overloaded and crash or make an error, an emergency can occur. Again in systems terminology, the Controller or Sensor elements, in such an event, are likely to be compromised, and demand the pilot become the Controller.

A final example is a huge military cargo plane. That kind of plane exemplifies where the Structure element is of greater importance than the Conversion or Transport element. It needs to carry huge amounts of material, but the weight of the loads needs to be checked and properly secured. Great care goes into ensuring the right materials are used in building the Structure or body of such a cargo plane so it can carry tanks, howitzers, helicopters, in its belly. If this isn't done, the Structural benefits of the plane – the fact it carries a lot of weight – can change from an advantage to a danger.

There are two (2) key points that emerge from the previous discussion:

1. Systems theory teaches us, first, that perfection is a false goal; and,

2. Dealing successfully with the inevitable and ongoing systems variations from one type of airplane to another – or, more importantly, from one person to the next, or more broadly from one system type to another, is key to understanding the situation at hand, in order to achieve our Goal.

Now consider your body as a system. In terms of your physical and emotional wellbeing, you must learn to be the Controller of your health. You must take responsibility for the Inputs into your system: your diet, your exercise, your sleep schedule, and the people you bring into your life. And in order to do that, you need to get the best information you possibly can, so you can choose what Inputs are right for YOU.

But that's not as simple as it sounds. Your goal is to optimize your health, but that's not the goal of the decision makers who create the environment you live in. Their goal is to optimize their profits. Your responsibility is to become your own life's Controller, but their objective is to seize that power for themselves and their corporations or government bureaucracies. Their goals, ultimately, are based on distracting and lulling you, so you don't take accountability and be the Controller of your health. They like it when you become a "dumb" consumer, and simply follow some fad diet, buy their latest bestseller, and use a one-size-fits-all protocol, or other bogus and irrational rules based on some mysticism, that is rooted in faith and belief that have nothing to do with your body or your particular system.

In order to achieve their goals they have plenty of resources at their disposal. They control the media, they control politics, they control science, medicine and health care, and they control the bankers that can pay for it all.

So what can you do about it? Begin by looking around and applying the concepts we've been discussing. Notice connections instead of seeing random rolls of the dice.

You can use your physical self to help with this. Do you have a headache? Why do you think that is? Is it because you're tense, or you didn't get enough sleep, or you drank too much? Or maybe you have no idea at all why you have a headache.

Mysterious though it may be, thinking about your headache, its causes, and your response to it can start you thinking about things from a systems point of view. Is there anyone who profits from your having a headache? Or who profits from how you try to get rid of it?

Thinking like that is a good way to start becoming the Controller of your body, your system, and your own life too. Yes, that's a start. There's much more to come.

CHAPTER TWO

Reductionism

Alex is a forty-one year old married man, the father of two children, who lives in New England. He has a twin brother and two sisters and is close to his extended family. He is 5'9" tall and weighs 196 pounds, 30 pounds more than when he played on his college tennis team. Alex works in the computer industry. He spends most of his days (and many of his nights) hunkered down in front of a monitor. The only exercise he gets is playing with his children, but they're mostly interested in electronic games.

Those are some facts about Alex, but who is he really? The truth is, he's many things to many people.

To his doctor, for example, Alex is a man who should lose weight and lower his slightly elevated blood pressure. The doctor has given him three months to accomplish this through diet and exercise. If that doesn't work, Alex will have to start taking medication.

Five years ago, on his first visit to this doctor, Alex shared a memory from his teenage years. He was home from school on a snow day, helping his father shovel the driveway. Then his father suddenly collapsed with chest pains, and Alex called the emergency hotline 911. The doctor knows that Alex's father has a pacemaker and that Alex doesn't want that for himself.

The doctor also knows that Alex, who inherited his mother's fair skin, has had surgery for a patch of squamous cell skin cancer on his nose. Alex has promised his wife and his mother that he will never again go fishing or do anything out in the sun without first covering himself with sunscreen.

But Alex is more than the collection of symptoms he presents to his MD. To his wife, he is a loving husband who likes to bake bread and make pasta for the family. He spends too much time on his computer. Sometimes he snores at night.

To his parents, Alex is a devoted son who calls regularly and is always available to help out. To his co-workers, he is a hard-working employee who has an intricate knowledge of the newest technology. To his twin brother, with whom he shares a close, but sometimes competitive, relationship, he is a best friend and a formidable chess opponent. To his children, he is "Daddy, daddy, play with me! I need more batteries! Will you fix this? Can we go to the park?" To his dog, he's the guy who throws a ball further than anyone else.

So who is Alex? There's no single answer. The dilemma of, "Who is he?" or for that matter, "Who am I?" is as old as time.

An ancient parable makes this point. A group of disciples approached the Buddha with some serious questions about whether the world is finite or infinite, and whether the human soul dies or lives on forever.

The Buddha replied, "Once there was an important raja (a king) who assembled all the blind men in his kingdom in a courtyard. In the center of the courtyard was an elephant. One at a time, each of the blind men was led forward to put their hands on the elephant's body. One man touched the head, another the tusks, another the ears. And so it went, with each man feeling a different part of the elephant.

After they were done, the raja asked of each of them, "What is this thing we call an elephant?"

The man who touched the head said, "An elephant is like a pot." The man who touched the tail said, "An elephant is a brush." The man who touched the tusks said, "An elephant is a spear." They each described the elephant according to what they touched. The Buddha used this story to teach the impossibility of absolutes. We all view the world differently, because we are all different.

For a systems biologist, there is a short – but complex – answer to questions like, "Who is Alex?" or "What is an elephant?" Alex is a system. Ditto the elephant. But we can't know the true nature of the system until we see it in its entirety by knowing not the parts, but the interconnections.

This brings up the important concept of *reductionism*. In 1687 Isaac Newton published his great work entitled *Principles of Natural Philosophy*. Since then, Western science has been based on a simple and reasonably reliable assumption: to understand something in the natural world, take it apart.

Want to understand a watch? Take it apart and examine the pieces. Want to figure out why an engine runs, or figure out how a human body functions? Look at the parts one at a time. If you understand the parts, you can understand the whole. It's certainly easy to understand why this approach can be so appealing. Some things are simply too complex and huge to grasp any other way. It's complicated so we reduce it down to its smaller parts. This approach is known as *reductionism*.

Let's follow reductionism to its logical conclusion. If it's informative to reduce something to smaller parts, wouldn't it be even more informative to reduce something to parts that are as small as possible? We can look at a tree and have some general understanding of what it is, but can we have a deeper understanding of the tree if we look at the chemistry of the leaves? Or even the atomic structure of the leaves, the bark, and the roots?

The answer to that is both yes and no. Quantum physics, for example, is concerned with the smallest possible particles in the universe. To the extent we can understand those infinitely small particles – which isn't easy – we can understand what the universe really is at the most basic level.

Great! But here's the problem. We don't experience the universe at the most basic level of its trillions of sub-microscopic parts. We experience it as an amalgamation of those parts that has become a vast interconnected system. It's true that atoms are almost completely empty space, but that fact isn't going to help you if you get hit by a car. The reductionist focus on separate parts can distract or even blind us to the reality of those parts as a whole system – especially when the whole system, as the saying goes, is somehow more than the sum of its parts.

Reductionist science has of course contributed greatly to human knowledge. But the limits of reductionism are apparent in our current health care establishment, with its high costs, uneven quality of care, and drug development protocols that are expensive and slow. Reductionism fostered the modern healthcare system that was able to respond well to a crisis, like an injury or an acute illness. But today there's a growing demand for a system that delivers prevention, can deal effectively with chronic conditions, and is considerate of the long-term effects of specific therapeutics, protocols, and procedures, on a personalized level.

The modern health care system came into being during the industrial era. It was structured to manage calamities of war, and the system itself followed a military model, with doctors as officers and nurses as enlisted personnel. Those conditions encouraged reductionist thinking. Wartime situations required a healthcare system that rewarded specialization and "magic bullet" solutions: a single drug, the right specialist, or the right procedure to address immediate and catastrophic events.

Reductionism was effective in that context, delivering life-saving solutions *after* the onset of disease or injury. But reductionism now pervades all aspects of the modern healthcare, including basic research, patient treatment and drug development. We are literally using a healthcare system designed for war and crises to manage the day-to-day healthcare of modern life, which should be primarily based on prevention.

Here's an example of how this works. My friend recently visited her internist, with a sinus infection. The internist sent her to an ENT - an ear, nose, and throat specialist. The ENT examined her and made recommendations for medication. My friend complained that a post-nasal drip making its way from the sinuses through her throat and into her lungs was giving her a bad cough. The ENT said he was sorry but the cough involved the lungs, and he didn't treat anything below the neck.

The reductionism of modern healthcare compels increasing specialization, where a problem is divided into many smaller problems. As medical consumers, we know how exasperating this can be. We know that we can't always divide our bodies up into parts. We know that the foot bone is connected to the anklebone and the anklebone is connected to the shin bone and the shin bone is connected to the knee bone. Yet, if we have a foot pain and a knee pain, we have to visit at least two different doctors, who in all probability are not consulting with each other to determine if there is a connection. This is one of the problems associated with a reductionist approach to health.

21st Century science is beginning to realize that a reductionist approach offers only part of the truth. When you connect a bunch of things, whether they are auto parts or human parts, something emerges that is greater and different than the sum of its parts. Take something as basic as a clock. If you take a clock apart, it's nothing more than a collection of odd assorted pieces. When it's put together in the right order, with the right connections, a clock assumes an almost magical function in terms of what it does and how a reliance on an accurate reading of time impacts your world. If this is true for a clock, imagine what happens when you are talking about a living organism, whether it is a tree, an animal, or a human being.

Systems thinking, and systems biology specifically, can help us understand health and illness as a dynamic interconnection of parts. It's not just the raw sum of their individual components, much less the parts by themselves. This is critically important, because more often than not, reductionist Controllers will show you only those parts of a system that they want you to see, because it leads you down a path that is convenient to them, not the truth.

A reductionist might tell you that taking a certain pill will reduce headache or muscle pain, and indeed it will. That same reductionist might not tell you that the pill can damage your kidney function.

Similarly, a reductionist analysis of the oil and natural gas mining process known as hydraulic fracking could show significant profit potential under certain market conditions. But fracking also seems to be related to an incidence of earthquakes in parts of the country that haven't had an earthquake for thousands of years. The larger system, of which fracking is a part includes both financial and seismological components.

The truth is that truth itself emerges not from one element of a system, but from the interconnections of the elements. Moreover, the interconnections themselves are an element of the system, and often the most important element.

Systems biology, and systems theory in general, recognizes that a system can't be understood by taking it apart. To understand a system or to understand any part of it, you must know how the parts relate to one another, and to the whole. That is a philosophical principle of system thinking.

A revolutionary principle of systems thinking is demanding to know how the parts relate and interconnect to the whole. If that information is withheld from you, you must find a way to get it. Remember, our Goal, collectively and individually is Truth, Freedom and Health, and settling for a small and mistaken shadow of truth like one of those blind men with flawed Sensors will only mislead us away from that Goal.

So, if we are committed to our Goal, then getting that information mandates a certain necessary action, but if those in control refuse to take action to give us that information, then you must take action to see that the action gets done – perhaps, as Malcolm X said, "By any means necessary."

CHAPTER THREE

Emergent Properties

Earlier I mentioned the two priesthoods of our present culture – reductionist science, which developed from a Western rationalist tradition of Isaac Newton and a quasi-Eastern neo-Buddhist self-help peace-and-love movement featuring gurus and motivational speakers.

I don't see myself in either of those categories. I'm an engineer, and engineers are primarily workhorses. We get the work done, while the priesthoods of East or West postulate and theorize. Engineers build things – and because of the constraints and imperfections of the physical world, whatever we build must be open to change and refinement.

More specifically, I'm a biological systems engineer, an electrical engineer and a mechanical engineer with advanced training in design. I see things as engineering systems spanning multiple domains and disciplines. Systems are based on connections and the *emergent properties* that arise out of those connections. To put it more poetically, an emergent property is a higher-level phenomenon that comes into being when lower level parts are connected in a specific way. In biological systems, that emergent property can be anything such as consciousness, one's weight, or even a particular ailment or disease. The underlying connections are always the key.

One theory is that consciousness itself emerges when enough number of interconnections takes place across millions of neurons in the brain. So from lower to higher life forms, given that the physical size of the brain and number of neurons varies, varying states of consciousness emerge, since the number of interconnections grows exponentially. Similarly, an ailment or disease emerges from the multitude of interconnections of many bad behaviors: bad food, no exercise, wrong "friends," stress, etc.

Let's see how this looks, from a biological level. In 2002, after more than a decade of research, the Human Genome Project completed sequencing of the human genome or DNA.

By now, anyone who has ever watched a police based drama on television has some idea of what DNA is. Our DNA, a genetic configuration unique to each of us, stores information and instructions on our personal characteristics. The genes in our DNA determine our eye color, how many teeth we have, the color of our hair, as well as tendencies toward developing certain illnesses. The Human Genome Project's goal was to identify all the genes in the human DNA along with their locations and their function. It was a massive undertaking.

When the Human Genome Project got under way, there were two key assumptions:

1. The difference or complexity between a human being and other organisms, such as a worm, was the number of genes in DNA; and,

2. If the entire human genome could be mapped, then manipulating the DNA could control any and all aspects of life.

Ironically, the Human Genome Project disclosed that not only were the two key assumptions wrong, but also that DNA may be relatively less important to our current and future states of existence. The scientists involved with the Human Genome Project originally believed that humans possessed a larger number of genes than other life forms. It was an understandable assumption: we have preeminence over other life forms; therefore we must have more genes. During the early stages of the Project, most expected that humans would have at least 500,000 to 1,000,000 genes. As time went on during the sequencing phase, the estimates changed to 100,000, then 50,000 then 30,000. Eventually it was revealed that we have the about the same number of genes as the lowly earthworm—somewhere in the neighborhood of 25,000.

Yet, we are so different. So clearly, the number of genes is not a measure of complexity. In short, an emergent property was revealed: we are more than our genes and, as humans, we have power over our destiny beyond the DNA we inherited from our parents and ancestors.

The scientific community reeled from this discovery. How was it possible that a worm, which looks so different from a human being, could have the same number of genes?

To help understand that question, we have to think about the function of our genes and, consequently, our DNA. People are often confused about the difference between DNA and genes. DNA, which is stored in the nucleus of all of our cells, is often likened to a set of blueprints or codes that contains the instructions necessary to construct other components of cells.

The discovery of DNA in the early 1950s by the British biologists James Watson and Francis Crick is one of the most celebrated achievements in the whole history of science. Watson and Crick asserted that DNA is completely "in charge." DNA is the central Controller of who we are and what we become.

Genes are the essential components of our DNA. They hold the secrets of what you are and what you will become, based on who came before you in your genetic line. Genes provide instructions for the creation of specific molecular configurations called proteins. These proteins are created outside of the cell nucleus, in what is known as the cytoplasm of the cell. In the cytoplasm, instructions from the genes arrive via a molecule called messenger RNA. The proteins are then synthesized in the cytoplasm.

Each protein has a particular function. The protein Insulin, for example, is critical in metabolizing or breaking down sugars. If you don't have enough insulin, you have a high likelihood of getting diabetes. This tendency to diabetes is something we inherit through our genes.

The so-called "central dogma" of Watson and Crick concerning DNA is as follows:

1. DNA, within the nucleus of each cell, stores the genetic information of who we are.
2. The genes in our DNA provide instructions through a molecule called messenger RNA (mRNA) to create proteins.
3. Proteins are created outside of the nucleus of our cells.
4. Proteins, the molecular machines of our body, interact or "dance" with each other in order to orchestrate different types of molecular pathways, such as metabolism, synthesis, etc.

Looking at this, we can see how DNA was believed to be the "mastermind" of the entire operation of life, giving rise to the successive effects of mRNA, proteins, and molecular pathways. It was a one-way street with DNA as the source; other elements were its effects.

The Human Genome Project ironically revealed that the complexity of human beings couldn't be explained by looking at our DNA alone. We especially need to consider the dance of proteins and molecules, known as *molecular pathways* that take place in the cytoplasm outside of the cell nucleus. These molecular pathways are the interaction of a set of proteins, each at particular concentration levels, working together to elicit a particular *cellular function* such as cell signaling, metabolism and transcription.

These cellular functions may even turn genes on and off, exerting a feedback effect to control gene expression. So, it's not just the genes in our DNA, located in the nucleus, that determines who we are, but the molecular pathways that are in constant activity across the nucleus and cytoplasm. For example, insulin interacts with multiple molecules to provide a complex set of molecular pathways to elicit the cellular function of metabolism.

A relatively new field of biological science called *epigenetics* has demonstrated some remarkable events. For example, prior to the Human Genome Project it was thought – and taught in biology classes – that because identical twins have the same DNA, they must both look the same. Consider eye color, where both identical twins have genes for blue eyes. The thinking was that, by definition, both twins would have blue eyes.

However epigenetics has shown that identical twins, having the exact same DNA to code for blue eyes, don't necessarily have to share the same blue eye color. How is this possible? Research in epigenetics shows that molecular pathways may serve as the *epigenome* to turn on and off the genes in the DNA that codes for eye color through a feedback mechanism, not yet fully understood.

This means that while DNA is important, the molecular pathways that occur across the nucleus (where the DNA is stored) and the cytoplasm of the cell may be more important in determining who we are, than the DNA itself.

On a personal scale, this means that you may have the gene for diabetes or certain types of cancer, but other factors are capable of suppressing the expression of that gene. These factors include diet, environment, lifestyle choices, what we think, and ultimately our state of consciousness, a theme of many ancient and traditional systems of medicine. These factors affect the molecular pathways, which in turn affect gene expression.

While the Human Genome Project gave us invaluable information on the genetic map of the human genome, including the location of various genes and their functions, it also provided us with knowledge that is even more far-reaching: We are more complicated than our genes. Who we are is an emergent property of the interconnection of our genes in the nucleus and the many molecules and proteins involved in molecular pathways inside and outside of the nucleus. These molecular pathways are influenced by multiple factors, which each of us can be the true Controller of, using our mind, body and spirit.

A systems approach aims to go beyond the DNA so that we can understand the entire organism and our relation to the environment and the cosmos. Systems Biology, based on the foundational history of molecular biology, attempts to link the dance of proteins and create a total understanding of human existence from DNA to RNA to Proteins, to single Protein-Protein Interactions, to Molecular Pathways to Cells, to Tissues, to Organs, to Organism, to Ecosystem – all the way to the furthest reaches of the Universe!

I know that the contents of this chapter may seem technical or even esoteric. But the purpose of the chapter is actually simple and straightforward. The purpose is to show that you are more than the sum of your parts, even at the most basic level of your physical and biological being.

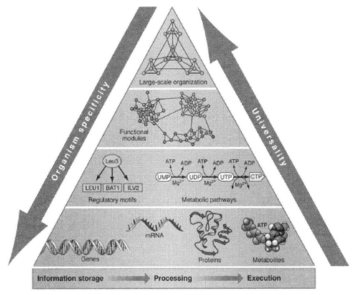

Pyramid of Life's Complexity
(Oltvai and Barabasi, 2002)

So don't let anyone convince you that your destiny can be revealed by any specific aspect of your identity – not by your height or your weight or your race or your educational history or your DNA. Those factors – which exist in you in unique proportions – are always interacting with an infinite number of other factors in your physical, emotional, and spiritual environment.

Emergent properties are constantly being born out of those interactions. You may think you can't play a musical instrument, but if you find the right teacher – or the right audience – you might play beautiful music. You may think you'll never fall in love, because you never have. But love can emerge when you meet the right person. In fact, this concept of "soul mates" is shared by spiritual traditions around the world.

Perhaps most importantly, the human experience of emergent properties can and should exist beyond our individual identities. It happens in our cells but it doesn't happen only in our cells. It happens also in the experiences we share with other people, and the collective actions that then become possible.

A revolution that unleashes all our abilities to fully experience Truth, Freedom and Health, is the ultimate possibility to advance humankind. It would be a revolution in all areas of being: in what we think, what we feel, and how we live. Although at this point it may not be possible to describe exactly what the revolution will look like, as the revolution progresses we will be able see it more clearly – and that in itself will be an emergent property of the revolution. And let me repeat what I said at the start of this chapter. I'm an engineer. I'm less interested in philosophizing about things than in making them happen.

Does that include making a revolution? The short answer is definitely yes – but in systems terminology another term for revolution is *phase transition*. That's the subject of our next chapter.

CHAPTER FOUR

Phase Transition

Phase transition is an important concept in systems theory. It often refers to the transformation of matter from one form to another – as when heats transforms solid ice to liquid water and eventually to gaseous steam. It's of course also true that phase transitions also occur in other areas – in the history of our species, and even in the lives of individual human beings.

In order to understand the role of phase transitions in human experience, it's helpful to first examine how those transitions take place in the physical world. Water coming to a boil is an often used as an example. Like many other phase transitions, that process is a combination of gradual, incremental change culminating in a sudden and distinct transformation.

At or near sea level, water boils at 212 degrees Fahrenheit. If you watch a pot of water being heated on a stove, there will be a relatively long period of time in which nothing seems to be happening. Then a few bubbles will form at the bottom of the pot, and not long afterward the water will suddenly transition into a full boil. The arc of the phase transformation seems to be slow, then slightly faster, and then almost abruptly when the required temperature is reached. Suddenly the water is no longer starting to boil; it actually is boiling.

Historical change seems to happen in much the same way. Dating back to the ancient Greeks, there were philosophers and early scientists who taught that the Earth revolved around the sun. The Indian astronomer Aryabhata proposed much the same thing in the fifth century AD. But the idea of heliocentrism did not really "come to a boil" in the Western world until Nicolaus Copernicus wrote *De revolutionibus* in the 16th century. Heliocentrism was by no means immediately accepted, but – considering how long the concept had actually been around – acceptance did happen quite rapidly.

But there is a supremely important difference between these two-phase transitions. Water coming to a boil is a purely physical process, but the Copernican transition was a change in consciousness. The Earth did not start going around the sun when Copernicus said it did. In fact, nothing was changed on the physical level. Instead, there was a change in people's thinking about physical reality that opened the door to enormous transformations in politics, religion, and science.

Initially this manifested as chaos. There were persecutions and executions by the Roman Catholic Church. There was an immense power struggle between the religious establishment and the rising influence of science, which the establishment (rightly) saw as a fundamental threat. But gradually the power of "self-organizing systems" took hold. This is the principle that instability in a dynamic system will gradually resolve back toward an equilibrium – which will remain in place until the next phase transition. Despite what we might think (or wish), equilibrium is actually the most vulnerable and temporary condition in any system. Phase transitions are the real order of the day, or even of eternity.

One of the most interesting – and also frustrating – aspects of phase transitions is how hard they are to anticipate. In the early 1950s, after World War II and the explosions of nuclear bombs, Americans seemed to know that big changes were coming. Predicting the future was a popular media topic, and the year 2000 was a frequent target date.

The predictions were virtually always wrong. Yes, phase transitions were coming but, no, they would not feature flying cars or rocket backpacks. Nor would cancer be cured, unfortunately. No one foresaw the advent of personal computers. No one mentioned the possibility of climate change. No one predicted that natural foods or running shoes would become billion dollar businesses and transform society.

But in the last few years something really extraordinary has happened, something unprecedented in human history. In the past, phase transitions were the product of brilliant minds and powerful societal forces. They developed slowly, outside the awareness of most people, and then they seemed to suddenly burst on the scene. Predicting them was difficult or impossible, and making predictions was mostly done for entertainment value.

Now, however, phase transitions can be manufactured! They can be sold. They can be shoved down people's throats by huge corporations whose marketing forces are absolutely irresistible to millions of people.

Walk down a busy street in any American city, or any city in the world for that matter. If five people are coming toward you, at least three of them will be using a cell phone, and it's likely all five will have one. Cell phones have taken over. They're everywhere. When people lose or break their cell phones, they experience serious withdrawal symptoms and become depressed until they get another one.

It's almost impossible to believe that as late as 1990 there was some question as to whether the cell phone would really catch on. Would people really want to be getting calls anywhere and everywhere? Wouldn't they feel like their privacy was being invaded? Would they actually want to watch videos and play games on a tiny screen?

Well, we now know the answer. The cell phone represents a genuine phase transition. It's changed everything. It's probably driven us crazy. But most importantly – and unlike phase transitions of the past – the cell phone is a product. It has a price tag. It generates profits for corporations and their executives. There's human consciousness behind it, mostly that of Steve Jobs, rather than a vast economic force like the rise of feudalism or the huge volcanic explosion in 1500 BC that doomed the Minoan civilization.

What does this mean for you? Let's put it in terms of systems theory. The power behind the scenes of phase transition is no longer some Big Controller in the sky. The intervals between phase transitions will no longer be thousands of years in length. Five hundred generations may have passed before it dawned on people that a stone could be sharpened into an axe head, but Bill Gates' dream of a personal computer in every home took less than twenty years. Plus, Bill Gates got rich. What did the inventor of the axe head get?

I found all this out through personal experience. My family had emigrated from India. When I invented email as a 14-year-old boy in Newark, New Jersey, my intention was to make work easier for the secretaries at the University of Medicine and Dentistry of New Jersey. I had no idea that the Raytheon Corporation and the whole academic-corporate-governmental power structure were intensely determined to be the Controller of the phase transition created by email.

They wanted to perpetuate their carefully formulated mythology of how innovation takes place, who does it, and for what purpose. Innovation had to be done by an employee of a major defense contractor, in the contractor's facility, using the contractor's equipment, and as an adjunct to a project for the government or the military. This was the history they wanted to control – and as George Orwell wrote, if you control the past you can control the present and the future.

The point is this: you have to make yourself the Controller of your own present and future. If you don't, there is some very powerful machinery that is set up to do that for you. You have to self-organize, for your own protection and wellbeing. You have the ability to do that and you need to use your ability to the fullest extent.

When you do that, you can begin to create a powerful emergent property, as we discussed in chapter three. And when enough people seize Control, that collective emergent property will become a phase transition of its own.

What will the world look like after that transition? That's of a very important question, and it's also a highly speculative one. Even Marx, who described history's economic cycles in such minute detail, refrained from any description of the world after "the withering away of the state."

But without venturing where Marx feared to tread, I have a clear vision of some key changes that this great phase transition will bring.

In the Introduction to this book, I referred to Truth, Freedom and Health as humanity's basic and legitimate goals. Right now, you are becoming aware of the fundamental principles that govern all systems. Your body is a system, and when it comes to Health, you have an opportunity to take revolutionary action, here and now, to be the Controller of your body, your system and find what is right for YOU, using the power of systems theory.

PART TWO

Your Body, Your System

CHAPTER FIVE

Know Your System

It's 7:30 a.m. on a frosty New England morning. There's a foot of new snow on the ground and, according to the weather channel, at six degrees, the temperature almost matches the time. Sarah is running late for her nine o'clock writing class, but before she can leave she has to do something about snow removal. She stayed on the phone past midnight talking to a friend about a new novel she read; Sarah became so engrossed in the conversation that she forgot to put her car in the garage.

Now, before she can go anywhere, she has to figure out how to get out of the driveway. Sarah hates the cold weather, and it takes her a long time to dress for it. She puts on long pants, a light thermal undershirt, a heavier shirt, a wool sweater, and a light down vest. She pulls wool socks and lined boots on her feet, wraps a thick scarf around her neck, puts a warm hat on her head before she finally covers herself with a long hooded down coat and rushes out the door.

Outside, Sarah sees several neighbors who are also busy dealing with the snow. She waves to James, who lives next door. He gives her a quick wave in return and yells out, "Stop running or you'll fall." James, whose driveway is remarkably snow free, always makes sure that nobody else on the block beats him in the snow removal department. James, who tends to be abrupt and a bit of a curmudgeon, approaches things very methodically and likes to shovel his driveway by hand according to some efficiency method he once shared with Sarah. She couldn't quite follow what he was saying, but it had something to do with incorporating exercise reps with snow removal. She is always amazed that James never seems to get cold. Today, James is wearing light cotton pants, a long sleeved cotton shirt and a light down vest. He has nothing on his head, but he is wearing light gloves. "Aren't you freezing," she yells out to him. "Nope," he answers. "You just have to keep moving."

Frank, the neighbor across the street, is also out with his new snow blower. "If you brush the snow off your car," he tells her, "I'll do your driveway. Frank isn't very talkative. All Sarah really knows about him is that he has a large extended family and seems to enjoy "taking care" of others. This morning, she is very grateful that she was in his line of vision and that he is offering his help. However, as grateful as Sarah feels, she still wishes that Frank would move a little bit faster.

When we look at Sarah, James, and Frank, we see that they are very different from each other, and that they approach life and its challenges differently.

These differences are larger than the obvious ones of gender and age. In systems terminology, Sarah is dominated by Transport forces; Conversion is front and center for James; In Frank, the forces of Structure are less obvious, but they are nonetheless dominant.

The forces of Transport, Conversion and Structure affect all forms of Matter, Energy and Information throughout nature. The strength of these forces varies from one life form to another. That strength also varies among individuals – including you – within a given species.

The importance of these variations is being recognized by Western medicine, as better diagnostic tools become available and as genome research reveals the individual character of human DNA. But the concept that every person's physiology is a system with an individualized balance of energies has existed for thousands of years. This became clear to me when I received a Fulbright grant that allowed me to return to India for study of the ancient health tradition known as Siddha.

The Siddhars – the term means "enlightened ones" – used their own bodies as experimental laboratories to understand the interaction of three essential forces which they called Vata, Pitta, and Kapha.

It's surprising – or maybe it's not surprising – that Vata, Pitta, and Kapha are exact parallels of Transport, Conversion, and Structure. Perhaps systems theory is simply a new terminology for an ancient wisdom tradition. Whether we see ourselves as combinations of Transport, Conversion, and Structure – or of Vata, Pitta, and Kapha – each of us is a shifting and individualized balance of these energies. It's a balance that needs to be continuously acknowledged, understood, and cared for.

What is your Natural System State?

As the three forces of nature interact within each of us, some of us have more Transport, others are strongest in Conversion, and still others are dominated by Structure. There are even a few individuals who have an almost equal presence of each. The varying proportion of these forces is one of the most essential ways in which we are different from each other.

Initially, you need to identify your own Natural System State. Once this has been done, the goal of supporting that state becomes possible. So what is your essential nature? Which forces give direction to your being?

Transport expresses itself as sensitivity to variations in flow, mobility, and movement. If Transport is your dominant force and that force is too high, you may feel nervous and agitated. If it's too low, you could feel very lethargic or depressed. Transport is in charge of everything that moves and is kinetic in our bodies, including the flow of energy and information. Because of this, Transport is regarded as the primary force without which Conversion or Structure could not function. When Transport is not functioning correctly, all the other forces can go awry.

Are you dominated by the force of Transport?

- o Do you have an exceptionally difficult time dealing with cold weather?
- o Do you move quickly and frequently juggle several activities at the same time?

- Do you think and talk quickly?
- Are you interested in fields such as communication and media?
- Do you prefer spontaneity over a set of routines and scheduling?
- Do you tend toward dry skin and hair or flaky scalp?
- Are you naturally prone to being thin or slight in size or have a relatively easy time losing weight?
- Are you happy that you are able to grasp new ideas and learn quickly but wish that you were able to remember more of what you learn?
- Are you in such a rush to "get going" that you can be overly impulsive and start working on projects without thinking things through?
- Do you sometimes skip meals or forget to eat?
- Do you have a basically optimistic and enthusiastic attitude?
- Do you have a tendency to become anxious or nervous?

Conversion manifests as sensitivity to variations in physiological processes such as metabolism and digestion, as well as analytical thinking and decision-making. If the forces of Conversion are not functioning well, you can experience health and emotional problems associated with the inability to convert and transform elements of Matter, Energy and Information.

Are you dominated by the force of Conversion?

o Do you really, really dislike heat and hot weather?

o Are you happiest when you, and those around you, stay on schedule?

o Are you detail oriented and exceptionally good at processing information and data?

o Do you usually think things through before taking any kind of action?

o Do you metabolize food quickly and efficiently?

o Do you like competition and view just about any kind of competition as an enjoyable challenge?

o Do you have a medium build and does your weight tend to fluctuate?

o When it comes to eating, do you prefer food that is on the bland side and/or do you find that your digestion goes awry eating spicy food?

o Do you have a big appetite and do you need to eat at regular intervals?

o Do you easily become impatient either with yourself or others?

o Do you enjoy taking ideas and transforming them to some kind of practical application?

o Are your eyes particularly sensitive to sunlight?

Structure is the principle of containment for matter, information, and energy. Men and women who are Structure dominant are naturally able to sustain and tolerate more than other people. Structure forces foster relaxation and calm, and an aura of security. But when Structure is out of balance it can manifest as stubbornness or isolation.

Are you dominated by the force of Structure?

o Are you big boned or do you have a broad body frame?

o Do you tend to be overweight or have a difficult time losing weight?

o Are you happiest when you can stay in one place and do not have to move around or travel?

o Are you aware of other people's needs and are you often called upon to help others?

o Are you not particularly bothered by either hot or cold weather?

o Do you almost take your strong energy and good stamina for granted?

o Do you get "lazy" and/or easily depressed?

o Is your preferred learning style slow and steady?

o Is one of your strengths your ability to retain what you've learned?

o Do you like to take your time and resist moving from one activity to another?

o Do you have problems with congestion or mucous such as sinus infections, asthma or colds?

o When you speak, do you try to be precise and make a point of saying what you think?

Summing up, all systems have a particular state in which they function optimally. But this state doesn't happen by itself. Careful observation and conscious action are required. We have to see things as they are, in order to create things as we want them to be.

CHAPTER SIX

Dealing with Disturbances

Obstacles and disturbances are part of any journey, including the journey of our lives. Once you become aware of your Natural System State, it's your responsibility to keep that as close as possible to the balance point of your life, despite any turbulence you encounter. Health is modulated by setting the Natural System State as your Goal. Recall our original feedback systems diagram:

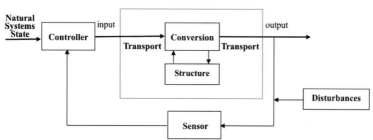

Closed loop system with Natural Systems State as the Goal.

The unfortunate fact is that at any given moment you are likely not operating at the Goal of your Natural System State. The Eastern traditions have long recognized this difficulty. Techniques such as yoga and meditation were developed in order to refine our Sensors and develop our intuitive understanding, so as to provide rapid feedback to the Controller so we remained on track, and closer to our Natural System State and avoided large deviations from our Goal, regardless of the nature of Disturbances. This became clear to me when I studied Siddha in India on a Fulbright grant and uncovered a direct correlation between the language used in Eastern spiritual practices and modern Western systems theory.

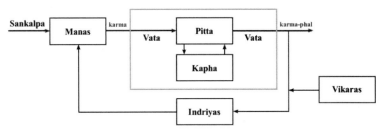

Regulatory Cyde of Siddha and Ayurveda.
(Ayyadurai, 2014)

As the diagram illustrates, given its resemblance to the closed loop system of modern control systems engineering, the ancient spiritual masters of the East were fundamentally systems scientists who simply used a different language to understand the world as a system. My research uncovered a "Rosetta Stone," which provides a bridge between their language and the modern terminology of systems theory.

Control systems engineering	Siddha and Ayurveda
Input	Karma
Output	Karma-Phal
Transport	Vata
Conversion	Pitta
Storage (Structure)	Kapha
Goal	Sankalpa
Controller	Manas
Sensor	Indriyas
Disturbances	Vikaras

Rosetta Stone of Siddha and Ayurveda.
(Ayyadurai, 2014)

So we do not have to choose between Eastern spiritual practices and Western objective science. We should embrace and use them both because at the core, their origin is in systems science, which is invariant across the ages. Integrating techniques across East and West is the key to unlocking the secrets of optimal mental, physical, and spiritual health, based on a systems perspective.

How are you right now?

How are you feeling today? Is everything going well in your life? Do you feel upbeat and cheerful or do you feel down in the dumps? Are you feeling healthy? Or are you catching a cold?

As a unique and dynamic person, you are not going to be feeling the same every day. Here are some questions to help you get a handle on what the forces of Transport, Conversion, and Structure are doing in your system right now. Your answers will help you determine which forces are "off-course."

You can then decide how you want to bring that force back into alignment using the Inputs discussed earlier.

Are your Transport forces undergoing disturbances?

- o Is your sleep pattern disturbed? Are you having trouble falling asleep or staying asleep?
- o Have you been making any noticeably impulsive decisions or do you find yourself talking almost non-stop?
- o Are you having issues with joint or arthritic pain?
- o Are you sometimes spacing out or are you having a difficult time concentrating or finishing projects?
- o Is cold weather bothering you even more than usual?
- o Are you sometimes forgetting to eat or are you losing weight?
- o Is your lower GI tract upset? Are you having bouts of diarrhea or constipation? Are you experiencing gas or a sensation of bloating?
- o How about your skin? Do you have any dry spots, chapped, or cracked skin?
- o Is your energy level noticeably uneven? Are you feeling depressed or do you have bursts of energy so intense that you have a hard time calming down?
- o Are your emotions on the overwrought side? Have you been feeling particularly anxious, jumpy, or overly excited?

Are your Conversion forces undergoing disturbances?

- o Are you experiencing strong feelings of jealousy or a need to get even?
- o How is your skin? Are you getting more rashes, acne, or cold sores than usual?
- o On a scale of one to ten, is your impatience level at about a twelve?
- o Is your food or liquid intake out of control? Do you feel ravenously hungry, or even a little sick to your stomach, if your meals are even a little late? Do you drink large quantities of water or other beverages?
- o Have you become noticeably sarcastic, competitive, argumentative, or critical of others? Are your friends telling you to 'chill out'?
- o Are you easily angered?
- o Are you having problems with your eyes? Are they bloodshot, strained, or do you feel you need even stronger sunglasses than usual?
- o Is your natural aversion to heat becoming more intense?
- o Are you having upper GI problems? Are you suffering from heartburn, GERD, or a sore throat that your doctor thinks is being caused by acid reflux?
- o Is your quest for perfection becoming even more intense? Are you putting too much pressure on yourself or others?

Are your Structure forces undergoing disturbances?

o Are you responding to stress by giving people the silent treatment or generally shutting them out of your life?

o Are you finding it almost impossible to start new projects or make changes in your life?

o Do you feel a need to accumulate more stuff you don't need?

o Are you having an exceptionally difficult time letting go of things ranging from people and emotions to old newspapers and unnecessary objects?

o Are you procrastinating? Do you have a list of things to do that you keep putting off?

o Are you generally feeling lethargic and dull?

o Do you have a white coat on your tongue?

o Do you want to sleep all the time?

o Are you having an impossible time keeping your weight under control? Do you find it impossible to resist carbs, chocolate, or other sweets?

o Do you seem to have even more mucous issues such as sinusitis, allergies, chest congestion or asthma attacks than usual?

By knowing which force or forces are disturbed, you can be the Controller, making adjustments to Inputs that will bring you back to your Natural System State. But the first step is to correctly assess what's wrong. What is the true nature of the disturbance? Be real. Don't look for an easy answer, neither in reductionist science nor reassuring mysticism.

CHAPTER SEVEN

Adjusting Inputs to Your System

"Garbage in, garbage out" was an early principle of computer science. It's should also be a maxim for anyone who wants to understand systems theory and apply it to their lives. If your Input is garbage, there's not much that can be done with it. But assuming you're bringing the right energies into your system, the next step is optimizing the forces of Transport, Conversion, and Structure that process and sustain those energies.

Controlling the Forces of Transport

Transport is expressed through movement. When it's in balance, Transport presents itself as joy, grace, agility and enthusiasm. Both systems theory and Siddha identify three Inputs as essential for Transport to function at an optimal level: warmth, rhythm and lubrication.

Stay Warm

Our bodies, particularly our muscles, work far more efficiently when they are warmed up before any kind of activity or exercise. Muscles contract and relax faster when they are warm. Warmth gives your muscles greater agility, speed, and strength. Warming up is like an insurance policy, decreasing the possibility of injury while also allowing you a greater degree of motion. If you are warm, your blood vessels are dilated, and this reduces stress on your heart and increases the flow (movement) of blood throughout your body. Blood is the key transporter of nutrients in your body. When you stay warm, your blood is able to be more efficient and deliver more oxygenated blood, making your entire system more effective to support motion at multiple levels. It also enables oxygen in your blood to be transported at a greater speed.

Your joints are key to movement and motion. Staying warm enables you to have a wide range of motion. Stiffness, for example, is a symptom that Transport is not working right. Warmth increases production of synovial fluids in your joints, serving to reduce friction, to support that range of motion. Greater range of motion gives you the greater confidence to try new things in a safe manner. Staying warm helps your body secrete the hormones that enable energy production, which is key to Transport. Exhaustion is another symptom telling us that the forces of Transport are not functioning right.

Movement can be erratic and chaotic, methodical and elegant, or graceful and intelligent. Staying warm enables nerve impulses to be transported at greater speeds, resulting in greater focus. This focus in turn will support the right level of concentration in a relaxed manner to provide support for graceful motion.

In order to thrive, Transport needs the Input of warmth. Think about your car on the coldest winter morning. Most of us will go out and warm it up before driving off. The warmth we are talking about is inner warmth, inside of the engine, inside of the car, inside of you. Warm friends, a warm home, and a warm disposition all fuel your inner forces of Transport. By doing those things that build such inner warmth, you directly support the optimal functioning of Transport.

Stay in Rhythm

A sense of rhythm is the ability to move your body to a regular beat. Rhythm or regularity is key to optimal motion and Transport. A person who dances well moves to a regular rhythm. A great drummer follows a great beat. Musicians often train with a metronome, an instrument that puts out a constant beat, to help them keep their rhythm. One of my mentors Frank Zane, the great body builder, taught me to lift weights to a metronome, or to a beat. When one does this, it makes it much easier, and more fluid. One can move and Transport with greater ease.

Because the force of Transport drives so many important body processes, it requires this level of regularity. Breathing, digestion and elimination are all dependent on proper rhythm and regularity. Having a regular schedule, eating at regular times, and sleeping and waking regularly are all about being in rhythm, which makes Transport far more effective. As someone said, "repetition is the mother of skill."

Siddha masters recommended that their students follow a schedule – early to bed, early to rise – routinized meal times, and play and work at particular hours. They were very demanding about the need for such regularity. In fact, in all spiritual practices, regularity is more important than the length of practice. Some people will meditate for 2 hours for a few weeks, and then stop, without any semblance of discipline. It is better to do less, but with consistency to achieve the best results. The highest level of rhythm and regularity is critical for the force of Transport.

In our breathing, the forces of Transport manifest themselves most clearly. Without breath our entire being ceases to exist. In the Bible, it is said that life began when God breathed into Adam's nostrils. The breath we have has a rhythm and regularity. That rhythm regularizes our pulse, our heart beat and our nerves. Emotions such as anger change our rhythm, and affect the forces of Transport. Every time we move or exercise, this is an exercise in breath. Breath is a gateway for us to see the force of Transport in action, and a way to measure our regularity, moment to moment.

Stay Lubricated

Smooth and agile motion is supported by lubrication. All machines move better when they are well lubricated. Think about it. Your car will not move without oil and regular oil changes. Nor will you. To support Transport, your body needs to be well lubricated. Lubrication supports our joints, enables cellular motion, lessens build-up of plaque in our arteries, and ensures that nerve impulses fire right.

Across a range of internal cellular processes, Transport needs lubrication. Without lubrication, the machinery of our bodies begins to squeak, get tight, rust, and motion stops. That squeaking door in your kitchen needs some oil. The stiffness in your joints would also benefit from some lubrication. Lubrication removes friction and ensures long-life of machinery, including your inner machinery.

The right kinds of oils and fats, and proper hydration support that lubrication. Wonderful research is being done and continues to be done on the value of different kinds of wholesome plant and animal based fats and oils. Doing your own research on them can prove to be invaluable. Healthy fats and oils play an overall role in supporting the forces of Transport. They contribute to an increase in energy and help us gain muscle mass. They also support the functioning of our heart, lungs, brain and digestive organs – all components involved in Transport. The right lubrication makes our internal motors of motion that move air, blood, electrical signals run with ease and minimal friction. Healthy fats help protect our heart, a motor-like pump, from cardiovascular diseases.

Our bones and skeletal structure keep us moving as we walk and run. Lubrication of the right kind has been shown to strengthen bone density and reduce incidences of fractures, so as we age, we can still keep moving. Your skin is a major organ of transporting fluids and substances such as hormones, lymph, and water. Hydration, which is a form of lubrication, is key to supporting movement of those fluids and substances to support the forces of Transport.

The right kind of lubrication also supports internal cellular signaling, and the right signaling is key to cellular communication. Wrong communication results in illness and disease. Repeated studies have shown the value of lubrication at the cellular level to protect against various forms of cancer. Lubrication protects our machinery from rusting – a process known in chemistry as oxidation.

That bicycle chain in your backyard has oxidized and is rusty. Put some oil on it, clean it up, and it's as good as new. Similarly, oils that are known as anti-oxidants can help remove the "rust" from our internal motors so Transport forces are able to glide smoothly. Nerve signaling, a type of cellular signaling, affects mood disorders. Stress affects nerve signaling and may result in increased depression and anxiety. The right kind of lubrication increases levels of serotonin in the body. Serotonin makes people feel good and puts them in a relaxed state. Being relaxed supports agile Transport.

Controlling the Forces of Conversion

The forces of Conversion are expressed as intensity and determination. When three key Inputs are present, Conversion presents itself as enterprising, brave, intelligent, ambitious, confident, and self-disciplined. These three Inputs are essential for Conversion to function at an optimal level: being cool, regulated and clean.

Stay Cool

Let's start with an enlightened awareness that intensity (fire) doesn't need more intensity (or fire). Fighting fire with fire doesn't work here. The process of Conversion does the job of converting Matter, Energy and Information from one form into another. These processes all require "heat." However, in order to operate efficiently, they also need proper cooling.

A nuclear reactor, which is able to convert nuclear fission to thermal energy, is a classic example of Conversion. But a nuclear reactor needs those big cooling towers we see when pictures of reactors are shown. Your hot kitchen needs an exhaust system to keep it cool; your computer needs a fan to keep it cool.

Men and women with rapid metabolism and fiery dispositions – expressions of Conversion in action – need to stay cool, in both mind and body, to balance their internal engines. Those with Conversion dominance need to look to the external world for ways to input cooling factors. This is different from those with a Transport dominance, who need to Input ways of increasing internal warmth.

Conversion dominant people need to avoid "hot situations" that can cause tempers to flare; they need to learn to "cool down" during those times when the intensity of action (during tough business negotiations, for example) becomes too extreme. Staying Cool ensures that you don't over-heat and burn up your internal engines, which are the power source of Conversion.

Warm-blooded animals sweat (like a human) or pant (like a dog) to dissipate heat through water evaporation. Sometimes it's easy just to cool off by going under a nice shaded tree or get some water on us. Other times it may be good just to take a vacation, "chill out" and go to cooler areas. Sometimes just sitting and watching the sunrise or sunset or other forms of Nature's beauty can serve to provide the cool to calm down and support the forces of Conversion, to remove the "heat."

Stay Regulated

The forces of Conversion are involved in the process of transformation and transduction. They convert energy from one form to another. The retinas in your eyes convert light, electromagnetic radiation, to chemical impulses which are transduced to "see" the world. The engine in your car converts chemical energy to rotational mechanical energy.

All of these involve many systematic and interconnected processes that need to be regulated correctly, with great sensitivity, to make sure that the inputs are converted to the right outputs.

If your retina does not transduce correctly, you get blurred vision. If your car engine's pistons are not regulated with the right mixture of fuel and air to fire correctly, your car's motion could be abrupt with backfiring. All engines need to regulate their activity from action to rest, from focused work to regular maintenance – in short they need to be in balance across the forces of motion and stillness.

Conversion can create a tendency to push too hard. They gravitate toward being on the go all the time, with extreme activity and little rest. If they don't learn how to regulate their activities, they run the risk of "burning up" and "burning out". Sometimes, this inability to regulate their own internal engines, results in an attempt to control everything, and everybody, in their environment. It would be better for them to learn how to control and regulate their own activities.

It can be difficult for a conversion dominant person to "let go" and relax, either by themselves or with others. Their tongues can become harsh and mean – an inappropriate way to control a situation, because in reality they are not able to control themselves. Extremes of this out-of-control behavior include throwing tantrums, becoming manipulative, all of which reflect a lack of self-regulation, which can backfire much like a car engine, whose internal pistons misfire. High performance jet engines are designed to function well. They are able to operate across a wide range of temperatures and altitudes. They can regulate their performance across a variety of conditions, can adjust and adapt. Conversion forces require proper regulation to ensure their optimal functioning.

Regulation includes setting bounds of operation. Those who are dominated by Conversion forces can achieve great success, if they are given, or create for themselves, internal and external boundaries. A high performance car also has its boundaries - if you "red-line" above a certain number of RPM's, the engine will conk out. The forces of Conversion operate well within their lower and upper bounds.

Work and rest are therefore equally important for these forces of Conversion. Forces of Conversion, like a motor can "be on" all the time, and not know when to stop. Men and women with strong Conversion forces have a tendency to overdo just about everything. They can work too hard, they can exercise too much, and they can overdo it with their attention to detail. Our Conversion dominant friends sometimes need to relax and stop competing. They need to learn to modulate their behavior, keeping everything more reasonable and moderate.

Regulating your behavior also implies being able to "surrender" and "go with flow" at appropriate times. Those with dominant Conversion forces can sometimes appear always to be on "high alert" in terms of a need to control the people and things in their environment. They need to learn how to regulate their behavior by stepping back and surrendering. It's essential to know when to stop, relax, rest, and shut down.

Stay Clean

Like any high performance engine, forces of Conversion thrive in a clean environment. This includes both high quality fuel and a clean internal mechanism. People dominated by Conversion need to be very careful about what they input into their bodies. Whole foods, organic, without preservatives, and without additives are wonderful because they provide "clean" fuel.

There is an emerging movement among pioneering food manufacturers in formalizing the definition of such clean foods through a newly developed Certified C.L.E.A.N. international standard, which I helped to facilitate using a systems-based approach that defines such foods as ones that have multiple attributes including being safe, non-GMO, organic, and having high bio-availability of nutrients. Keeping an eye out for such clean foods can serve to support Conversion.

Food combining is another wise strategy for ensuring effective transformation within our digestive systems. Slow-cooked foods, in many ways pre-digested, make it easy for our internal engine to absorb nutrients. In addition, regular and moderate fasts allow our engines to clean and heal themselves by support the body's own self-healing processes.

Controlling the Forces of Structure

Structure brings stability, and stability is essential for survival. Men and women in whom Structure is dominant tend to have stability in their own lives and they like to provide it for others as well. The three Inputs that encourage Structure's optimal performance are: being dry, active and flexible.

Stay Dry

The force of Structure provides containment and support. When a home is built, the foundation represents the Structure force that holds the entire house. If the foundation (or basement) is damp or wet, the building's entire infrastructure is at risk.

Excessive dampness in your body's foundation can show up as cysts, tumors, chronic sinus infections, and yeast infections. Dryness can also have the benefit of slightly raising the body's temperature, creating a structural environment that is resistant to viruses and bacteria. A dry sauna, for example, can be ideal for supporting Structure.

Stay Active

Use it or lose it. Any physical structure, including the human body, gets stronger the more it gets used and stimulated. If you don't use your muscles, your skeletal structure, you atrophy. Structures that are not used are vulnerable to decay and rust. Various types of stimuli are critical in keeping a structure activated.

At the cellular level, the cell membrane and cytoskeleton, support structure of the entire cell. Nature ensures that this structure is under constant stimuli to keep it vigilant and active. Such activity increases the number of macrophages. Macrophages enhance the immune system and support structure by killing invading bacteria and viruses.

Physical activity also increases blood flow, allowing antibodies to move through your system and attack and remove bacteria and viruses. For those who suffer from inflammation, anti-inflammatory cytokines, which are the cell-to-cell signaling molecules, are themselves activated by physical activity. These molecules have a beneficial effect in promoting anti-inflammatory effects. This is one of the important benefits that come from being active because chronic inflammation causes most of the degenerative diseases such as cancer.

The forces of Structure provide framework and inertia. This inertia can also result, at its extremes, in laziness, moodiness, and immobility. Sometimes those who are dominant in the forces of Structure "just don't feel like moving." Inertia and a lack of movement can contribute to a sense of depression or lethargy. Exercise and physical activity stimulates neurotransmitters in the brain to make one feel happier, less moody, and less depressed. Inertia is also implicated in osteoporosis, a structural disorder that causes bone loss. Exercise and physical activity is prescribed as a treatment for those who have osteoporosis or are in danger of getting it because it can help prevent and arrest the problem.

In order to hold things, Structure itself requires containment. The tendency to "holding on" often spells out issues with weight. Being active is a great controlling and modulating factor to manage one's weight. There is no better cure for the inertia and laziness of Structure forces than to boost one's energy level through physical activity. Diseases such as diabetes manifest when the forces of Structure go to its extremes of containment. Being active can be help deal with this condition. Activity helps makes the body more sensitive to insulin, to support burning of glucose e.g. calories. This helps to lower blood glucose and stop sugar spikes. Diabetics who exercise have been shown to need less insulin or medication than those who don't.

People with Structure dominance can also become too complacent and reliant on the status quo. They have a tendency to not want to "let go" of anything, including relationships and objects. They can "hold on" to relationships, situations, and things that no longer have value in their lives. Activity—getting out in the world, meeting new people, and trying new things—is a way of fighting this tendency.

Stay Flexible

Structure contains the elements of water and earth. Structures composed of water and earth can get stuck, muddy, swampy, and immobile. The most powerful structures in the world are not rigid, but flexible. If something is too hard, it can become brittle, and just shatter and break. In civil engineering, when larger structures are built, particularly in earthquake zones, they are designed to sway and be flexible; sometimes they are even put on rollers, so they will move with the wave of the earthquake. The largest modern skyscrapers in the world now actually flex like pine grass in the wind.

This is a wonderful example of how flexibility can provide additional strength and make structures strong enough to withstand even the most powerful of Nature's forces. Similarly, flexibility is key for someone who is Structure dominant. If you become too stiff, you too can break or fall apart by life's continual and ongoing disturbances and changes. If you become too set in your ways, you might end up feeling as though you are stuck in a quagmire that resembles nothing so much as a muddy swamp.

Flexibility gives structures greater strength. Joints and fascia are particularly improved by flexibility. Blood flow can be increased by flexibility exercises such as stretching, which removes toxins and waste products that can cause a structure to "squeak" and get stiff.

Stretching the joints also results in improved blood flow, which, in turn, can cause slight increases in tissue temperature; this supports circulation and increases the flow of rich nutrients to the joints creating greater elasticity and higher levels of structural performance.

Flexibility allows structures to be more effective in dealing with environmental disturbances. My grandmother used to tell a story of two kinds of trees. One tree would bend when a river flooded and was able to go back to its original shape once the waters receded. The other tree would resist the flood and would ultimately be broken, ripped out from its roots. Structures that bend are more likely to survive.

Scientists have repeatedly shown how flexible structures can adjust themselves to reduce drag. It is clear that that unlike rigid structures for which an increase in velocity causes a squared increase of drag, the increase in drag for a flexible object is significantly lower.

***

Above all, be aware of the core message of this chapter. It's your responsibility – and your opportunity – to become fully aware of the dominant energies of your being, and your Goal is to keep them in balance to support your Natural System State, not someone else's. Remember too that balance is not a passive state. It's achieved through strong action, and strong action is required to sustain it as well. There's a teaching by Vivekananda, one of India's contemporary spiritual masters, that alludes to this. Despite his metaphysical orientation, Vivekananda advised his students that if there was a choice between doing 50 pushups and meditating for 50 minutes, do the pushups!

CHAPTER EIGHT

External Adjustments:
You are NOT the Universe

The concept that connected elements can form a closed, self-sustaining unit is a principle of systems theory. But no system is completely self-contained. Every system is part of a larger system that ultimately includes, on one end, the most distant galaxies and on the other end trillions of infinitely small sub-atomic particles. As a result, we can't really understand a system until we see it in the larger context.

That accuracy isn't always easy to obtain. For example, a document known as the *Almagest*, written around the year 100 A.D., is one of history's most influential treatises on astronomy. The author was Claudius Ptolemy, a Roman citizen who lived in Egypt. The *Almagest* offers a complete and highly detailed description of the universe as a system, based on observable phenomena such as the rising and setting of the sun.

At the core of the complex Ptolemaic system, however, is a single basic premise: the planet Earth does not move. Instead, everything in the universe moves around the planet Earth. Consequently, although the Ptolemy's Almagest does explain the observable phenomena, the explanation is wrong. The system is comprehensive, convincing, and even beautiful, but it is factually incorrect.

Despite this incorrectness, a geocentric model of the universe connected with deep human needs, and also with issues of political power. A system that places human beings at the center of the universe is obviously reassuring, or perhaps flattering, compared to viewing ourselves and our planet as just another grain of sand on a huge seashore.

In addition, Ptolemy's viewpoint seemed in accord with Biblical teachings. Therefore it supported and justified the chief interpreter of the Bible – the Pope of the Roman Catholic Church.

Today we have our own doctrines, many of which can be just as convincing as the Ptolemaic system. The concept of genes being the central Controller of our lives was one of them. Today, we know that this is not true. Who we are emerges from the molecular interaction of genes, proteins, and many other molecules, across a massive network of systems of systems, from cell to tissue to organ all the way to our whole body and all the external systems that surround us.

In fact our bodies are not just composed of our 10 trillion human cells but also and more importantly of 1000 trillion foreign microorganisms. We are not just "our" body, but are carrying a whole ecosystem of us and 100 times more foreign travelers (or are they carrying us?) We are NOT at the center of ourselves, but a peripheral part of something much larger. We are only 1/100th of "ourselves."

Danger however arises when vast political, social, and financial power becomes connected to a particular dogma, which then must be seen as "obvious" and "beyond question."

The truth is, nothing should be obvious and beyond question. Life is dynamic and changing. Nothing is constant. In Woody Allen's film *Annie Hall*, his character turns to Diane Keaton and says, "A relationship is like a shark. It has to constantly move or it dies."

We are constantly moving, or we ought to be. We need to expand our awareness and continually take action. In Part Two, we've focused on balancing internal energies. But our inner selves exist in an external context. It's not enough to take responsibility for eating healthy and getting enough sleep. Becoming preoccupied with your own self-development and maintenance is a real danger if it leads to ignoring the world at large.

The plain fact is, there is injustice in the world and history's most evolved human beings have taken action against it. In the New Testament's Gospel of Luke, even Jesus said, "I came to set the world on fire and I wish it were already burning."

If you want to use tools like Your Body, Your System® (YBYS) to know your system state, how disturbances affect your health, and how adjustments can help you achieve better health, this is great. You will at least take matters into your hand and be a revolutionary in understanding your body as a system. However, know that this is just the beginning. You are NOT the center of creation, just as the Earth is not the center of the Universe. You are a very small part of a system with many interconnections. It's not enough to buy organically grown foods, and to condemn GMOs. We have to look deeper. What companies make money from GMOs? How are those companies connected to academia and government?

Being a revolutionary seeking Truth, Freedom and Health means being accountable to all areas in any area of your life. There is little benefit in perfecting yourself if you allow governments or corporations to degrade the world around you. We can accept the rule of politicians and demagogues, of reductionist doctors and New Age gurus, and just hope for the best. Or we can collectively know our bodies and ourselves as interconnected systems. We can start taking local action, which can ultimately magnify its effects as a global Phase Transitions – Revolutions.

Remember that your own wellbeing is both an end and a means. Even Buddha returned to the world when he saw that his enlightenment was not sufficient. When enough people do likewise, the universal system, of which we're all a part, will at last reach a collective fulfillment.

PART THREE

The Revolution

CHAPTER NINE

The Imitation of Life

In the early 20th century the pragmatist philosopher William James compared the world to a bunch of stones poured out on a table. Looking at the stones, different people may have entirely different impressions.

One person might count the stones and conclude that the number of stones was the most important thing about them. Someone with a more artistic sense could find patterns in the stones, like the image of an animal. A mystic might say that the stones are only an illusion we're all sharing.

William James states that, from a purely intellectual standpoint, none of these observations can be called false. They're all equally true as long as they exist only as thoughts in the minds of the observers.

But if someone actually tries to do something with the stones beyond just thinking about them, the situation changes. The arrangement of the stones might look like a dog, but we can't take it for a walk. Or we might think that the stones are an illusion, or that the table is an illusion, or even that everything in the world is an illusion – but if we jump out of the window, it won't be an illusion when we hit the ground.

An engineer is someone who would try to make something useful out of the stones. An engineer might try to connect the stones so that they became a paperweight or an ashtray or – if there were enough stones – the pavement of a street. In short, an engineer would identify a purpose for the stones. It may be that the purpose existed beforehand, or possibly the engineer is creating it from the start. To the engineer, that distinction doesn't really matter. The engineer will make the stones part of a system.

In Chapter One, we defined a system as "a set of objects or energies working together for a specific goal or purpose." That may seem like a reasonable description of a wristwatch or even a university, but how far can we extend it? Is a bunch of stones a system, or how can it become one? Is human history a system? Does history have a goal? Does the universe have a purpose? Does nature behave as an engineer, with a directed goal and purpose?

These are profound questions. Some very important scientists would answer with an emphatic "no." Steven Weinberg was awarded the Nobel Prize for physics in 1979. One of his best known quotes is, "The more we know of the cosmos, the more meaningless it appears." This seems to suggest that believing there is a purpose to the universe is a primitive concept – and as we learn more about the universe, we get further and further away from that belief.

Questions about purpose also exist in other areas of science. Jean Baptiste Lamarck, for example, a French naturalist, wrote that animals could alter their physical and genetic characteristics during their lifetimes, in order to serve specific purposes. A giraffe, for example, driven by its objective of easier access to food could lengthen its neck in order to stretch for leaves more effectively, and the characteristic of a longer neck would then be passed on to its offspring,

More than fifty years later, in 1859, Charles Darwin proposed a different theory of evolution based on a fundamental randomness. Darwin's principle of natural selection does not teach that giraffes evolved long necks in order to eat leaves from the tops of trees. Instead, one day a genetic accident took place and a giraffe with a longer neck was born. That accident gave the long-necked giraffe an evolutionary advantage; it was better able to survive and thrive. When it reproduced other long-necked giraffes, they too benefitted from that advantage and eventually all giraffes had long necks. But according to Darwin the process began with a random genetic mutation that became an inherited characteristic. The mutation did not come into being because of any desire, purpose, plan, or intention.

My work in organizational and biological systems has provided me with a unique insight, a "middle path" that resolves the contradiction between Darwin and Lamarck. Goals, intentions, desires – whether at the macro or micro level, across all spatial and temporal scales of any system – are not just random, but emerge from the interaction of a system within itself, and also from its external system interactions. This means that goals themselves are an emergent property.

While Lamarck may have not gotten it right, Darwin's notion that everything is random is also incorrect. The reality is that Darwin's giraffe did not get a long neck from pure randomness, nor did Lamarck's giraffe get its neck from stretching upward for leaves. Instead, the interaction of multiple systems resulted in the "goal" of the giraffe wanting to get a longer neck. The interaction of the genes, the environment, the ecosystem, the trees, and countless other systems resulted in the emergence of that goal. In fact, data repeatedly and consistently shows that if it were pure randomness, Darwin's giraffe would have taken much longer to appear, and likely never would have appeared at all. This has been one of the kinks in Darwin's work that has allowed religious "creationists" to attack his theory of evolution.

Once again, a systems approach that recognizes the nature of systems interacting and unfolding onto themselves reveals that goals and purposes are emergent properties. This point, though subtle, must not be underestimated. Take a moment to absorb this principle, which resolves many of the deepest issues of destiny and free will. *Our personal goals and desires are themselves emergent properties of our interactions with ourselves and the systems that surround us.*

My desire, my need, and my purpose to expose corruption and to fight against exploitation – while at some level under my control – is also something I am compelled to do because of my unique path in life. That compelling desire is an emergent property of myself as a system, which has interacted with a multitude of other systems within systems, many of which are beyond my control. Your journey is also such.

For all of us – as a system of human beings on this planet, who interact with many other systems – collective goals may emerge. Goals for Truth, Freedom and Health? Or for Profit, Control and Vanity? Whatever it might be, the Goal is what the system's Controller modulates, until that Goal is achieved.

The concept of *telos* – Greek for "objective" or "purpose" – has been debated over the years. While Karl Marx did not address the ultimate fate of the universe, he did see a clear direction and end point for human economic and social behavior. Marx taught that we are inexorably heading toward a kind of utopia – an ideal era of freedom and equality for everyone. But in all his many thousands of pages, Marx describes neither what this will actually look like, nor the origin of that "goal" or purpose. Perhaps he would have argued that no one living now is capable of describing it, any more than an ant can describe the geography of South America. Marx's inability to define the dynamics and source of his system's goal has been exploited by many in the reactionary and liberal bourgeois academic priesthood to slander, discredit and undermine Marx's vast contributions.

Today, advocates for so-called intelligent design assert that there is indeed a plan, and that someone or something is pulling the strings of nature. This view is discredited by mainstream science because intelligent design advocates do not give a clear rational explanation for such a plan. However, the nascent science of epigenetics is showing that genetic characteristics do not exist entirely independent of interactions with the external environment. Experimental evidence from biological research is demonstrating that goals themselves are an emergent property of system interactions. Epigenetics demonstrates that specific events and interactions across multiple systems can turn an animal's genes on and off, with dramatic consequences in the animals behavior.

This was documented in an experiment at McGill University, in which a group of mice was bred for a gene that mandated docile behavior. It was found, however, that when their mothers did not lick subsets of the mice after birth, the mouse pups exhibited agitation and aggression. More importantly, molecular pathways turned genes on and off at the cellular level in those mouse pups. This altered their genetics in ways that were later transferred to their offspring, making the offspring also aggressive.

From a systems perspective, this means that a mouse's behavioral "goal" of anger or serenity is not written in stone in its cells. Instead, the mouse's behavior and even its genetic characteristics *emerge* from the interactions of the various parts of its existence as a system. The system's "goal" is an emergent property and its final purpose depends on the various system interactions.

In his philosophy of history, Marx was like someone who holds up an acorn and says, "Look, this is going to turn into an oak tree." To a person who knew nothing about how trees develop, this would seem impossible and absurd. How could a huge tree be contained in a tiny seed? How could something so large emerge from something so small?

Those are good questions. Actually, that acorn emerges as a tree only when it interacts with and becomes part of a much larger system. The acorn must be planted in the ground, and it must be nourished by rain, and sunlight. It is from those multiple systems' interactions that the acorn's "goal" to become a tree emerges.

Marx believed that there is a system in human history, just as there is in acorns turning into oaks. This wasn't a matter of morality or aesthetics. When Marx wrote, little was known about the foundations of systems theory. But today, based on those foundations, it is self-evident that a system exists in economics just as it does in nature – and the defining attribute of a system is the purposeful movement toward a final goal. This attribute emerges from the system's interaction with itself and with the systems that surround it.

The Greek word *mimesis* is important for understanding this systems-based approach to civilization's development. It provides a foundation to appreciate the insights that Marx elucidated nearly 200 years ago. Mimesis means imitation. Bio-mimesis is the imitation of natural systems in order to achieve human goals.

Comparing human history to the acorn-oak continuum is a biomimetic concept. Marxism took a natural process like evolution and translated it into action in the realm of human affairs. Just as a newborn infant changes into a full-grown adult, Marx envisioned society transforming from hunter-gatherers to farmers to industrial workers and capitalist masters – and ultimately into people who after many centuries at last fulfill the destiny of humanity.

Examples of bio-mimesis are easy to find both in history and in the contemporary world. The British World War Two fighter plane called the Spitfire, for example, had wings designed to replicate the wings of a seagull. Velcro uses thousands of tiny hooks like those of thistles and burrs. Engineers study natural systems to extract principles from which they can engineer new systems. Since we are part of nature, it makes sense that the best systems we create are those that follow nature's engineering principles, honed over billions of years of trial and error.

Similarly, by understanding your body, a biological system, you can extract and experience the foundational engineering system principles of Transport, Conversion, and Structure that the body uses to achieve and sustain goals. The goals include growth in your early years, defense against illness or infection later on, and survival for as long as possible.

So far, so good. But there's a certain aspect of the natural world that needs to be emphasized here. It's a principle of nature that demands *mimesis*. It needs to be recognized and imitated in the important areas of our lives. We do not live in a biological or behavioral vacuum. Every aspect of our existence emerges from the principle of mimesis, the imitation of nature.

CHAPTER TEN

Beyond the Center

A critical question now arises: who directs the Goal of a system? For many years, a deep and underlying assumption is that a Goal is controlled from "the center outward" or "from the top down." According to this line of thought, a small, centrally organized entity issues directives to an external realm in the periphery, and that's how great things happen. From a biomimetic perspective, biology for nearly fifty years called this the "central dogma theory," originally put forth by James Watson and Francis Crick, the discoverers of DNA. The nucleus was described as the central Controller that directs the goals of the entire cell. However, all this changed in cellular biology around 2002, as I referenced in Chapter Three:

> *The Human Genome Project revealed that the complexity of human beings cannot be explained by looking at our DNA alone. We especially need to consider the dance of proteins and molecules, known as molecular pathways that take place in the cytoplasm outside of the cell nucleus.*

This may seem to concern only biology, but science is not separate from history or politics. When Galileo argued for a heliocentric solar system, nothing changed on the physical level. The sun seemed to rise and set just as it always had. So why was the Catholic Church profoundly threatened by Galileo's doctrine?

It was the philosophical and political implications of heliocentrism that caused the uproar. It was the idea that mankind was not the center of the universe. Therefore the Church, which cast itself as the central force in people's lives, was not the center of the center.

Galileo asserted that human life was happening on the periphery. Our world was no longer the center. The Church was literally marginalized, pushed off to the side of the solar system in a way that seemed to fundamentally diminish its power.

In the quote above about the Genome Project, the periphery is also being elevated at the expense of the center. The cytoplasm and the cell membrane, not the nucleus of the cell, is where the action is. This insight will not cause me to be arrested by the Holy Inquisition as happened to Galileo, but here too the human instinct toward "top down" thinking is called into question.

Faced with a new or mysterious phenomenon, the human imagination seems to jump to a specific conclusion: there must be a center of power; there must be a central leader; there must be an Inside that takes precedence over the Outside.

Or maybe it's not the human imagination that defaults into that viewpoint. Maybe someone or something occupies the center, and then promotes that occupation as the natural state of things.

And people are usually ready to believe that. It seems so simple. There's a leader and there are followers. There's a king and there are his subjects. There's a cell nucleus and there's the rest of the cell.

But I want to say loud and clear that, first, this way of thinking is a gross oversimplification of the natural world. It's an erroneous and false observation of bio-mimesis, and the opposite of reality, just as the Earth is not the center of the solar system. Secondly, it has dangerous and destructive political implications.

I know this from firsthand experience. When the revolution in high technology was bursting onto the scene in the 1970s, the military-industrial-academic complex naturally wanted to promote itself and position itself at the center of that revolution. The most important innovations had to come from that center so that, among other things, the public could see that its billions of tax dollars were well spent.

Toward this end, an engineer employed by the Raytheon Corporation, a major defense contractor, was cast as the inventor of email. Since email is arguably one of the most important developments in the history of human communication, the Raytheon engineer – his name was Ray Tomlinson – was cast into this role. He seemed perfect for the part. He came across as a brilliant tinkerer who invented email without any sense of its importance. He had an "aw shucks" manner and if he didn't' have a white plastic pocket guard in the pocket of his plaid shirt, it definitely seemed like he should have.

Despite its appeal to Raytheon and the powers-that-be, there was significant and deliberate misinformation embedded in the Ray Tomlinson storyline.

He did not, for example, invent anything like email as we all know it and use it. Instead, he simply edited a pre-existing computer program so a user could append text to a file on another computer. He introduced the @ sign as a way to distinguish one computer from another. But, the @ sign is not email, no matter how many millions of dollars Raytheon may spend in their public relations and marketing efforts to make it so.

Instead, the email system now used around the world, with all its many editing, forwarding, and downloading features, was invented by a 14 year old boy named Shiva Ayyadurai, who was interning at the University of Medicine and Dentistry of New Jersey, and wrote 50,000 lines of code in response to a challenge to create an electronic equivalent of the paper-based interoffice memo system. This included features such as Inbox, Outbox, Folders, Attachments, Memo ("To:," "From:," "Subject:," "Date:," "Cc:," "Bcc:"), Address Book, etc. — the now familiar components of every email system.

But these facts were and still are absolutely anathema to the currently dominant historians of high tech innovation. The facts have to be suppressed, and if they can't be suppressed they have to be discredited and ridiculed. The truth is just totally unacceptable.

Why is it unacceptable? Because it questions and subverts the dearly held, profit-based myth of how innovation takes place, where it happens, and (most importantly) what kind of people are responsible for it. An immigrant, low-caste, high school kid from India, working in Newark, New Jersey (one of the poorest cities in the United States) is just too outside the centralized paradigm – especially when, as the years passed, he refuses to "know his place" and keeps telling the truth about what happened.

There are several ironies in this situation. First, maintaining a centralized organizational model is costly to business, government, and academia. There's a steep price for ignoring everyone outside the consecrated inner sanctum. Conversely, there can be big rewards for looking elsewhere. But to the ruling overlords, control is more important than opportunity. Those in power want to maintain power over the system. They willingly shoot themselves in the foot as long as they can maintain Controller status.

However, if we want to build organizations that are in resonance with nature – biomimetic organizations – then we need to accurately observe how biological systems respond to and process information. If you burn your finger with a match, your brain doesn't ignore the sensation and treat it as irrelevant. Intelligence at the periphery – in your finger – directs your body to take action immediately to address the injury at its site, without needing central command and control from the brain.

At the cellular level, the cell membrane, at the periphery of the cell, is where the cell interacts with the external world including viruses, drugs, foods, and other molecules. Those interactions at the cell membrane drive internal cellular reactions within the cytoplasm, directing the cell to turn genes on and off in the nucleus. This contradicts the concept of DNA as the central command and control authority issuing unilateral commands, as Watson and Crick proposed.

In addition to its importance in cellular biology, this also has implications for organizational behavior.

In many companies, when an "injury" to the organization occurs at the "periphery" – otherwise known as the customer call center, which in effect is the "service membrane" – those in central command and control set irrational objectives based on maximizing profit by reducing costs. If customers call a company's 800 number, most companies focus on "resolving the issue" fast by doing anything possible to end the call in 90 seconds or less.

A widely reported brake pedal incident with Toyota is an example of this. Despite many emails and customers' phone calls, the issue was ignored. The problem finally received widespread attention when people were dying in major accidents. Toyota paid the US government 1.2 billion dollars to avoid criminal charges, and also lost billions in share value overnight.

However, there are biomimetic organizations that exploit how nature truly behaves and responds. Some time ago I worked with the Nike Corporation, which was using EchoMail, another of my inventions. EchoMail employed sophisticated AI to read, analyze, respond to, and route email from customers. I realized that Nike was a rare organization that treated customer service calls as a feedback resource instead of an annoyance to be ended as quickly as possible. Nike saw their customer service personnel, their service membrane, as front line direct access to their customers, even though customer service personnel were far from the central command and control center of the CEOs office.

Nike made use of information from the periphery, which was viewed as a source of innovation. EchoMail was used to intelligently route emails and calls. Complaints about certain shoes, for example, were Transported to product engineering, which used that feedback to Convert advances in shoe design. The Structure of Nike enabled innovation.

Successful companies leverage bio-mimesis and make the principles of Systems Theory – Goal, Input, Transport, Conversion, Structure, Output, Disturbances, Sensors, Controller – the basis of the organization. The objective is not just corporate profit, but social profit and service to a broader set of stakeholders including employees, customers, local community and society. These companies have Sensors to observe the Output of their responses. They use that information to adjust their system's Transport, Conversion and Structure elements in order to achieve larger Goals.

Transport originates in an organization's creative thinkers. Their job is to be imaginative and uninhibited. Then a variety of individuals – including engineers, sales staff, and executive decision-makers – perform the Conversion of those creative ideas into tangible value. All this takes place within the Structure of the organization provided and maintained by accountants, attorneys, and administrators.

In all areas of life, and very noticeably in business, a phase transition is now taking place in which the energy of Transport is located in the periphery, at the service membrane, rather than at the center of an organization. This is apparent, for example, in the Indian dairy cooperative Amul, which is jointly owned by more than

3.5 million associates. Amul changed India from a milk-deficient nation into one of the world's largest milk producers, a transformation known as the White Revolution. This is one of the most astonishing developments in recent business history, more impressive in many respects than the rise of Microsoft or Apple.

Yet Amul is mostly unknown in the Western world, and the reason for that is very simple. It's because Amul is not happening in the Western world. It transcends the conventional command and control model of most organizations. Amul is an example of how those in the periphery, at the "membrane," the edges, have self-organized to create a system that is "profitable" to all its stakeholders in the true meaning of the word. This self-organization defies the centralized, reductionist business model.

That outdated and exploitative system has to change, and it will change. The Internet has erased traditional borders between nations. The population of the Western world is aging and declining, while rapid change of all kinds – demographic growth, technical innovation, political influence – is taking place in Asia, South America, and Africa. This is the murmuring of the periphery asserting itself on a multi-national scale in the same way that the cell membrane is the genuine location of the incredible energy of Transport in every microscopic human cell.

I'm proud to be taking part in this transition. As an immigrant to the US from India, I am part of the macro demographic shift that is now taking place and one that will accelerate in the coming years.

On a smaller scale – even a microscopic one – my company called <u>CytoSolve</u> addresses the fact that the siloed and dysfunctional model of the trillion-dollar pharmaceuticals industry reliant on a feudal academic research framework is broken and archaic.

CytoSolve provides a revolutionary paradigm for drug development, using an information-centric, systems-based "in silico" approach, that enables the scalable and dynamic integration of molecular pathway models, by enabling collaborative research. CytoSolve is in the "cloud" and integrates and couples scientific research to create a "collaboratory."

Like Amul, CytoSolve's approach is revolutionary. It provides millions of biological researchers – whether in large organizations, or small institutions, or working independently – with a means to collaboratively engage problems in medicine that simply cannot be solved in the current insular and centralized academic model. CytoSolve itself follows bio-mimetic principles by celebrating the periphery. On a practical note, it provides a feedback system process that will completely eliminate the need for animal testing in drug development.

The email I invented in 1978 was the electronic emulation of the mail communications system. Similarly, CytoSolve is the electronic version of the molecular communication system, and its impact on medicine will likely have the same impact as email did on communication.

CHAPTER ELEVEN

After the Revolution

As I mentioned, even Marx, who described history's economic cycles in such minute detail, refrained from description of the world after "the withering away of the state."

But now, fully armed with facts, let's venture where Marx feared to tread, I have a clear vision of some key changes that this great phase transition will bring.

In the Introduction to this book, I referred to Truth, Freedom, and Health as humanity's basic and legitimate goals. In my opinion, this is likely the Goal of a large majority of humankind. This is not to say that other goals do not exist – including Profit, Control, and Vanity for those currently in power. But when our aspirations toward Truth, Freedom and Health are finally achieved, here are some of the changes I'm sure that we'll see.

> ➢ **Truth:** Knowledge will no longer be seen as belonging only to tenured academics with advanced degrees bestowed upon them by institutions funded by government and corporate bureaucracies. Just like the rest of

the world, intellectual life will be dynamic, challenging, and open to constant re-evaluation and revision. Truth will not be defined according to the current three-stage system of pronouncement by priesthood "authority," coverage by media, and eternal fossilization on Wikipedia.

➢ **Freedom:** Society will recognize that the spark of phase transition can and does begin anywhere. Anyone can strike the match. Innovation won't be touted as an offshoot of the military-industrial-academic complex, nor will innovators be denied recognition based on country of origin, race, religion, gender, or sexual orientation. Innovation will not be a scarcity controlled and anointed by a few. The enormous waste of human talent caused by prejudice and greed will be over. Everyone will participate, and everyone will benefit. Everyone will also have the right to bear arms as a practical matter of self-defense, and also as a statement that power will not be centralized in government forces.

➢ **Health:** Care and understanding of the human body will no longer be tied to the protocols and profit motives of drug makers and large hospitals. Medical treatment will not be based on a warfare model of crisis management and metaphors of victory or defeat. People will be informed and inspired to actively participate in healthcare decisions. One-size-fits-all treatments will be recognized as hopelessly out of date, and as science advances a truly individualized practice of medicine will emerge.

Overall, the future will be marked by decentralization of Input and Output – that is, decentralization of both resources and results. Education, healthcare, and government will move in the direction of a bio-mimetic paradigm and away from a corporate or bureaucratic model. This will be a movement toward the periphery, where the majority of humankind exists.

While we all rejoice in the Internet and its incredible opportunities, we must realize that it is still centralized. A few major telecommunication companies, search engine providers, and high-tech companies still control the actual networks, and the dissemination and organization of information. This centralization of power in what ought to be a decentralized paradigm contradicts our freedom of opportunity online.

Remember the Egyptian revolution during the Arab Spring? At the height of the movement, when workers were willing to take to the streets and join the students, the dictator Hosni Mubarak simply made a single phone call to Vodafone, one of the biggest telecommunication conglomerates. Vodafone shutdown the entire network in minutes: no more tweets, posts, or texting.

Real freedom will come when we as citizens take control of networks, and when we own them individually and collectively. The technology for such citizen networks is already here. You and I and our communities can create our own *mesh networks*, using hardware that we can locate on our roofs and in our homes. When this takes place, we will all become nodes of a network on the periphery, free of centralized control. This collective can emerge without the need for any center. This will be a true bio-mimetic model, resonating organically from the authentic nature of the electronic medium. And once again, the technology for this is available now. Further innovation will always be welcome, but is not necessary here.

Nature employs Transport, Conversion, and Structure to achieve tangible goals that emerge from self-organization of complex system interactions. Those principles can also benefit less tangible issues such as happiness in emotional relationships, or career satisfaction, or your ability to influence the world in which you live.

We've spoken about the fact that every system needs an objective. We've also seen how Karl Marx, the great advocate of revolutionary change, did not provide a description of what the world would look once the ultimate revolution had been accomplished.

But the absence of that description did not mean that the revolution should not take place. In fact, optimism that the goal will be reached – whatever it may turn out to look like – has got to be present in order for change to happen. There have been disappointments in the past, there have been mistakes, there have even been catastrophes – but this is what happens in a feedback system. Learning needs to take place, course corrections need to happen, and next time can be different.

114

There is a story of a student in search of enlightenment who traveled hundreds of miles to consult a renowned Buddhist monk. The student crosses rivers and traverses sandy deserts. Finally he climbs a steep mountain and finds a small hut at the summit. Entering the hut, he sees the monk meditating in a lotus position on the floor. But then the monk looks up expectantly, as if he had been waiting for the student to arrive.

The student then tells the monk why he has come. He has attempted many occupations over the years and nothing has worked out. His relationships have also been unsuccessful. He has very little money. His life has been extremely difficult.

"I've failed at everything," he tells the monk, hopelessly. The monk considers for a moment. Then he says, "That was then. This is now."

Every great religion has a story like this, and so do the revolutionary traditions of East and West. In that context, the purpose of this book has been to present revolution not as a single explosive event, but as a self-correcting system moving toward an objective.

In the near term, that objective can be to understand your body and your health from a systems perspective and to take positive action.

In the longer view, you can apply that same perspective to create genuine revolution in all areas of life.

You can and you should. You have nothing to lose but your chains.